NAME:

MOBILE NO.

EMAIL:

BABY'S NAME:

ADDRESS:

BABY'S PICTURE

DATE: _____ ○ Mon ○ Tue ○ Wed ○ Thur ○ Fri ○ Sat ○ Sun

NOTES TO NANNY _____

Wake Time	am	Last Fed At:	am
	pm		pm

DIAPERS			
TIME	DRY	WET	DIRTY
	○	○	○
	○	○	○
	○	○	○
	○	○	○
	○	○	○
	○	○	○
	○	○	○
	○	○	○
	○	○	○
	○	○	○

FEEDING	
TIME	OUNCES

SLEEP	
START TIME	END TIME

PLAY
○ reading & language
○ music/singing
○ art/crafts/motor skills
○ playtime with toys
○ outdoor time
○ other: _____

SUPPLIES NEEDED

MEDICATIONS	
TIME	TYPE & AMOUNT

NOTES TO PARENT

MOOD
○ happy   ○ fussy
○ sleepy   ○ sick
○ quiet   ○ grumpy
○ other _____

DATE: _____   ○ Mon ○ Tue ○ Wed ○ Thur ○ Fri ○ Sat ○ Sun

NOTES TO NANNY _____

Wake Time	am	Last Fed At:	am
	pm		pm

DIAPERS

TIME	DRY	WET	DIRTY
	○	○	○
	○	○	○
	○	○	○
	○	○	○
	○	○	○
	○	○	○
	○	○	○
	○	○	○
	○	○	○
	○	○	○

FEEDING

TIME	OUNCES

SLEEP

START TIME	END TIME

PLAY

○ reading & language

○ music/singing

○ art/crafts/motor skills

○ playtime with toys

○ outdoor time

○ other: _____

SUPPLIES NEEDED

MEDICATIONS

TIME	TYPE & AMOUNT

NOTES TO PARENT

MOOD

○ happy   ○ fussy

○ sleepy   ○ sick

○ quiet   ○ grumpy

○ other _____

DATE: _____   ○ Mon ○ Tue ○ Wed ○ Thur ○ Fri ○ Sat ○ Sun

NOTES TO NANNY _____

_____

Wake Time	am	Last Fed At:	am
	pm		pm

DIAPERS

TIME	DRY	WET	DIRTY
	○	○	○
	○	○	○
	○	○	○
	○	○	○
	○	○	○
	○	○	○
	○	○	○
	○	○	○
	○	○	○
	○	○	○

FEEDING

TIME	OUNCES

SLEEP

START TIME	END TIME

PLAY

○ reading & language

○ music/singing

○ art/crafts/motor skills

○ playtime with toys

○ outdoor time

○ other: _____

SUPPLIES NEEDED

MEDICATIONS

TIME	TYPE & AMOUNT

NOTES TO PARENT

MOOD

○ happy   ○ fussy

○ sleepy   ○ sick

○ quiet   ○ grumpy

○ other _____

_____

DATE: _____   ○ Mon ○ Tue ○ Wed ○ Thur ○ Fri ○ Sat ○ Sun

NOTES TO NANNY _____

Wake Time	am	Last Fed At:	am
	pm		pm

DIAPERS			
TIME	DRY	WET	DIRTY
	○	○	○
	○	○	○
	○	○	○
	○	○	○
	○	○	○
	○	○	○
	○	○	○
	○	○	○
	○	○	○
	○	○	○

FEEDING	
TIME	OUNCES

SLEEP	
START TIME	END TIME

PLAY

○ reading & language

○ music/singing

○ art/crafts/motor skills

○ playtime with toys

○ outdoor time

○ other: _____

SUPPLIES NEEDED

MEDICATIONS	
TIME	TYPE & AMOUNT

NOTES TO PARENT

MOOD

○ happy   ○ fussy

○ sleepy   ○ sick

○ quiet   ○ grumpy

○ other _____

6

DATE: _____ ○ Mon ○ Tue ○ Wed ○ Thur ○ Fri ○ Sat ○ Sun

NOTES TO NANNY _____

Wake Time	am	Last Fed At:	am
	pm		pm

DIAPERS			
TIME	DRY	WET	DIRTY
	○	○	○
	○	○	○
	○	○	○
	○	○	○
	○	○	○
	○	○	○
	○	○	○
	○	○	○
	○	○	○
	○	○	○

FEEDING	
TIME	OUNCES

SLEEP	
START TIME	END TIME

PLAY
○ reading & language
○ music/singing
○ art/crafts/motor skills
○ playtime with toys
○ outdoor time
○ other: _____

SUPPLIES NEEDED

MEDICATIONS	
TIME	TYPE & AMOUNT

NOTES TO PARENT

MOOD	
○ happy	○ fussy
○ sleepy	○ sick
○ quiet	○ grumpy
○ other	_____

DATE: _____ ○ Mon ○ Tue ○ Wed ○ Thur ○ Fri ○ Sat ○ Sun

NOTES TO NANNY _____

_____

Wake Time	am	Last Fed At:	am
	pm		pm

DIAPERS

TIME	DRY	WET	DIRTY
	○	○	○
	○	○	○
	○	○	○
	○	○	○
	○	○	○
	○	○	○
	○	○	○
	○	○	○
	○	○	○
	○	○	○

FEEDING

TIME	OUNCES

SLEEP

START TIME	END TIME

PLAY

○ reading & language

○ music/singing

○ art/crafts/motor skills

○ playtime with toys

○ outdoor time

○ other: _____

SUPPLIES NEEDED

MEDICATIONS

TIME	TYPE & AMOUNT

NOTES TO PARENT

MOOD

○ happy ○ fussy

○ sleepy ○ sick

○ quiet ○ grumpy

○ other _____

_____

DATE: _____ ○ Mon ○ Tue ○ Wed ○ Thur ○ Fri ○ Sat ○ Sun

NOTES TO NANNY _____
_____

Wake Time	am	Last Fed At:	am
	pm		pm

DIAPERS

TIME	DRY	WET	DIRTY
	○	○	○
	○	○	○
	○	○	○
	○	○	○
	○	○	○
	○	○	○
	○	○	○
	○	○	○
	○	○	○
	○	○	○

FEEDING

TIME	OUNCES

SLEEP

START TIME	END TIME

PLAY

○ reading & language

○ music/singing

○ art/crafts/motor skills

○ playtime with toys

○ outdoor time

○ other: _____

SUPPLIES NEEDED

MEDICATIONS

TIME	TYPE & AMOUNT

NOTES TO PARENT

MOOD

○ happy   ○ fussy

○ sleepy   ○ sick

○ quiet   ○ grumpy

○ other   _____

9

DATE: _____ ○ Mon ○ Tue ○ Wed ○ Thur ○ Fri ○ Sat ○ Sun

NOTES TO NANNY _____
_____

Wake Time	am	Last Fed At:	am
	pm		pm

DIAPERS			
TIME	DRY	WET	DIRTY
	○	○	○
	○	○	○
	○	○	○
	○	○	○
	○	○	○
	○	○	○
	○	○	○
	○	○	○
	○	○	○
	○	○	○

FEEDING	
TIME	OUNCES

SLEEP	
START TIME	END TIME

PLAY
○ reading & language
○ music/singing
○ art/crafts/motor skills
○ playtime with toys
○ outdoor time
○ other: _____

SUPPLIES NEEDED

MEDICATIONS	
TIME	TYPE & AMOUNT

NOTES TO PARENT

MOOD
○ happy   ○ fussy
○ sleepy   ○ sick
○ quiet   ○ grumpy
○ other _____

DATE: _____   ○ Mon ○ Tue ○ Wed ○ Thur ○ Fri ○ Sat ○ Sun

NOTES TO NANNY _____

Wake Time	am	Last Fed At:	am
	pm		pm

DIAPERS			
TIME	DRY	WET	DIRTY
	○	○	○
	○	○	○
	○	○	○
	○	○	○
	○	○	○
	○	○	○
	○	○	○
	○	○	○
	○	○	○
	○	○	○

FEEDING	
TIME	OUNCES

SLEEP	
START TIME	END TIME

PLAY
○ reading & language
○ music/singing
○ art/crafts/motor skills
○ playtime with toys
○ outdoor time
○ other: _____

SUPPLIES NEEDED

MEDICATIONS	
TIME	TYPE & AMOUNT

NOTES TO PARENT

MOOD
○ happy ○ fussy
○ sleepy ○ sick
○ quiet ○ grumpy
○ other _____
_____

DATE: _____   ○ Mon ○ Tue ○ Wed ○ Thur ○ Fri ○ Sat ○ Sun

NOTES TO NANNY _____

Wake Time	am	Last Fed At:	am
	pm		pm

DIAPERS

TIME	DRY	WET	DIRTY
	○	○	○
	○	○	○
	○	○	○
	○	○	○
	○	○	○
	○	○	○
	○	○	○
	○	○	○
	○	○	○
	○	○	○

FEEDING

TIME	OUNCES

SLEEP

START TIME	END TIME

PLAY

○ reading & language

○ music/singing

○ art/crafts/motor skills

○ playtime with toys

○ outdoor time

○ other: _____

SUPPLIES NEEDED

MEDICATIONS

TIME	TYPE & AMOUNT

NOTES TO PARENT

MOOD

○ happy   ○ fussy

○ sleepy   ○ sick

○ quiet   ○ grumpy

○ other _____

DATE: _____   ○ Mon ○ Tue ○ Wed ○ Thur ○ Fri ○ Sat ○ Sun

NOTES TO NANNY _____

_____

Wake Time	am	Last Fed At:	am
	pm		pm

DIAPERS

TIME	DRY	WET	DIRTY
	○	○	○
	○	○	○
	○	○	○
	○	○	○
	○	○	○
	○	○	○
	○	○	○
	○	○	○
	○	○	○
	○	○	○

FEEDING

TIME	OUNCES

SLEEP

START TIME	END TIME

PLAY

○ reading & language

○ music/singing

○ art/crafts/motor skills

○ playtime with toys

○ outdoor time

○ other: _____

SUPPLIES NEEDED

MEDICATIONS

TIME	TYPE & AMOUNT

NOTES TO PARENT

MOOD

○ happy   ○ fussy

○ sleepy   ○ sick

○ quiet   ○ grumpy

○ other   _____

DATE: _____   ○ Mon ○ Tue ○ Wed ○ Thur ○ Fri ○ Sat ○ Sun

NOTES TO NANNY _____

Wake Time	am	Last Fed At:	am
	pm		pm

DIAPERS

TIME	DRY	WET	DIRTY
	○	○	○
	○	○	○
	○	○	○
	○	○	○
	○	○	○
	○	○	○
	○	○	○
	○	○	○
	○	○	○
	○	○	○

FEEDING

TIME	OUNCES

SLEEP

START TIME	END TIME

PLAY

○ reading & language

○ music/singing

○ art/crafts/motor skills

○ playtime with toys

○ outdoor time

○ other: _____

SUPPLIES NEEDED

MEDICATIONS

TIME	TYPE & AMOUNT

NOTES TO PARENT

MOOD

○ happy   ○ fussy

○ sleepy   ○ sick

○ quiet   ○ grumpy

○ other

_____

DATE: _____ ○ Mon ○ Tue ○ Wed ○ Thur ○ Fri ○ Sat ○ Sun

NOTES TO NANNY _____

Wake Time	am	Last Fed At:	am
	pm		pm

DIAPERS				FEEDING		SLEEP	
TIME	DRY	WET	DIRTY	TIME	OUNCES	START TIME	END TIME
	○	○	○				
	○	○	○				
	○	○	○				
	○	○	○				
	○	○	○				
	○	○	○				
	○	○	○				
	○	○	○				
	○	○	○				
	○	○	○				

PLAY

○ reading & language

○ music/singing

○ art/crafts/motor skills

○ playtime with toys

○ outdoor time

○ other: _____

SUPPLIES NEEDED

MEDICATIONS

TIME	TYPE & AMOUNT

NOTES TO PARENT

MOOD

○ happy   ○ fussy

○ sleepy   ○ sick

○ quiet   ○ grumpy

○ other   _____

DATE: _____ ○ Mon ○ Tue ○ Wed ○ Thur ○ Fri ○ Sat ○ Sun

NOTES TO NANNY _____

Wake Time	am	Last Fed At:	am
	pm		pm

DIAPERS

TIME	DRY	WET	DIRTY
	○	○	○
	○	○	○
	○	○	○
	○	○	○
	○	○	○
	○	○	○
	○	○	○
	○	○	○
	○	○	○
	○	○	○

FEEDING

TIME	OUNCES

SLEEP

START TIME	END TIME

PLAY

○ reading & language

○ music/singing

○ art/crafts/motor skills

○ playtime with toys

○ outdoor time

○ other: _____

SUPPLIES NEEDED

MEDICATIONS

TIME	TYPE & AMOUNT

NOTES TO PARENT

MOOD

○ happy   ○ fussy

○ sleepy   ○ sick

○ quiet   ○ grumpy

○ other   _____

_____

DATE: _____   ○ Mon ○ Tue ○ Wed ○ Thur ○ Fri ○ Sat ○ Sun

NOTES TO NANNY _____

Wake Time	am	Last Fed At:	am
	pm		pm

DIAPERS			
TIME	DRY	WET	DIRTY
	○	○	○
	○	○	○
	○	○	○
	○	○	○
	○	○	○
	○	○	○
	○	○	○
	○	○	○
	○	○	○
	○	○	○

FEEDING	
TIME	OUNCES

SLEEP	
START TIME	END TIME

PLAY

○ reading & language

○ music/singing

○ art/crafts/motor skills

○ playtime with toys

○ outdoor time

○ other: _____

SUPPLIES NEEDED

MEDICATIONS

TIME	TYPE & AMOUNT

NOTES TO PARENT

MOOD

○ happy   ○ fussy

○ sleepy   ○ sick

○ quiet   ○ grumpy

○ other _____

17

DATE: _____   ○ Mon ○ Tue ○ Wed ○ Thur ○ Fri ○ Sat ○ Sun

NOTES TO NANNY _____

Wake Time	am	Last Fed At:	am
	pm		pm

DIAPERS			
TIME	DRY	WET	DIRTY
	○	○	○
	○	○	○
	○	○	○
	○	○	○
	○	○	○
	○	○	○
	○	○	○
	○	○	○
	○	○	○
	○	○	○

FEEDING	
TIME	OUNCES

SLEEP	
START TIME	END TIME

PLAY
○ reading & language
○ music/singing
○ art/crafts/motor skills
○ playtime with toys
○ outdoor time
○ other:

SUPPLIES NEEDED

MEDICATIONS	
TIME	TYPE & AMOUNT

NOTES TO PARENT

MOOD	
○ happy	○ fussy
○ sleepy	○ sick
○ quiet	○ grumpy
○ other	

18

DATE: _____   ○ Mon ○ Tue ○ Wed ○ Thur ○ Fri ○ Sat ○ Sun

NOTES TO NANNY _____

Wake Time	am	Last Fed At:	am
	pm		pm

DIAPERS

TIME	DRY	WET	DIRTY
	○	○	○
	○	○	○
	○	○	○
	○	○	○
	○	○	○
	○	○	○
	○	○	○
	○	○	○
	○	○	○
	○	○	○

FEEDING

TIME	OUNCES

SLEEP

START TIME	END TIME

PLAY

○ reading & language

○ music/singing

○ art/crafts/motor skills

○ playtime with toys

○ outdoor time

○ other: _____

SUPPLIES NEEDED

MEDICATIONS

TIME	TYPE & AMOUNT

NOTES TO PARENT

MOOD

○ happy   ○ fussy

○ sleepy   ○ sick

○ quiet   ○ grumpy

○ other   _____

DATE: _____   ○ Mon ○ Tue ○ Wed ○ Thur ○ Fri ○ Sat ○ Sun

NOTES TO NANNY _____

Wake Time	am	Last Fed At:	am
	pm		pm

DIAPERS

TIME	DRY	WET	DIRTY
	○	○	○
	○	○	○
	○	○	○
	○	○	○
	○	○	○
	○	○	○
	○	○	○
	○	○	○
	○	○	○
	○	○	○

FEEDING

TIME	OUNCES

SLEEP

START TIME	END TIME

PLAY

○ reading & language

○ music/singing

○ art/crafts/motor skills

○ playtime with toys

○ outdoor time

○ other: _____

SUPPLIES NEEDED

MEDICATIONS

TIME	TYPE & AMOUNT

NOTES TO PARENT

MOOD

○ happy   ○ fussy

○ sleepy   ○ sick

○ quiet   ○ grumpy

○ other _____

DATE: _____   ○ Mon ○ Tue ○ Wed ○ Thur ○ Fri ○ Sat ○ Sun

NOTES TO NANNY _____

Wake Time	am	Last Fed At:	am
	pm		pm

DIAPERS			
TIME	DRY	WET	DIRTY
	○	○	○
	○	○	○
	○	○	○
	○	○	○
	○	○	○
	○	○	○
	○	○	○
	○	○	○
	○	○	○
	○	○	○

FEEDING	
TIME	OUNCES

SLEEP	
START TIME	END TIME

PLAY
○ reading & language
○ music/singing
○ art/crafts/motor skills
○ playtime with toys
○ outdoor time
○ other: _____

SUPPLIES NEEDED

MEDICATIONS	
TIME	TYPE & AMOUNT

NOTES TO PARENT

MOOD	
○ happy	○ fussy
○ sleepy	○ sick
○ quiet	○ grumpy
○ other	_____

DATE: _____   ○ Mon ○ Tue ○ Wed ○ Thur ○ Fri ○ Sat ○ Sun

NOTES TO NANNY _____

Wake Time	am	Last Fed At:	am
	pm		pm

DIAPERS

TIME	DRY	WET	DIRTY
	○	○	○
	○	○	○
	○	○	○
	○	○	○
	○	○	○
	○	○	○
	○	○	○
	○	○	○
	○	○	○
	○	○	○

FEEDING

TIME	OUNCES

SLEEP

START TIME	END TIME

PLAY

○ reading & language

○ music/singing

○ art/crafts/motor skills

○ playtime with toys

○ outdoor time

○ other: _____

SUPPLIES NEEDED

MEDICATIONS

TIME	TYPE & AMOUNT

NOTES TO PARENT

MOOD

○ happy   ○ fussy

○ sleepy   ○ sick

○ quiet   ○ grumpy

○ other _____

DATE: _____ ◯ Mon ◯ Tue ◯ Wed ◯ Thur ◯ Fri ◯ Sat ◯ Sun

NOTES TO NANNY _____
_____

Wake Time	am	Last Fed At:	am
	pm		pm

DIAPERS

TIME	DRY	WET	DIRTY
	◯	◯	◯
	◯	◯	◯
	◯	◯	◯
	◯	◯	◯
	◯	◯	◯
	◯	◯	◯
	◯	◯	◯
	◯	◯	◯
	◯	◯	◯
	◯	◯	◯

FEEDING

TIME	OUNCES

SLEEP

START TIME	END TIME

PLAY

◯ reading & language

◯ music/singing

◯ art/crafts/motor skills

◯ playtime with toys

◯ outdoor time

◯ other: _____

SUPPLIES NEEDED

MEDICATIONS

TIME	TYPE & AMOUNT

NOTES TO PARENT

MOOD

◯ happy   ◯ fussy

◯ sleepy   ◯ sick

◯ quiet   ◯ grumpy

◯ other _____

DATE: _____   ○ Mon ○ Tue ○ Wed ○ Thur ○ Fri ○ Sat ○ Sun

NOTES TO NANNY _____

Wake Time	am	Last Fed At:	am
	pm		pm

DIAPERS

TIME	DRY	WET	DIRTY
	○	○	○
	○	○	○
	○	○	○
	○	○	○
	○	○	○
	○	○	○
	○	○	○
	○	○	○
	○	○	○
	○	○	○

FEEDING

TIME	OUNCES

SLEEP

START TIME	END TIME

PLAY

○ reading & language

○ music/singing

○ art/crafts/motor skills

○ playtime with toys

○ outdoor time

○ other: _____

SUPPLIES NEEDED

MEDICATIONS

TIME	TYPE & AMOUNT

NOTES TO PARENT

MOOD

○ happy   ○ fussy

○ sleepy   ○ sick

○ quiet   ○ grumpy

○ other _____

24

DATE: _____ ○ Mon ○ Tue ○ Wed ○ Thur ○ Fri ○ Sat ○ Sun

NOTES TO NANNY _____

Wake Time	am	Last Fed At:	am
	pm		pm

DIAPERS

TIME	DRY	WET	DIRTY
	○	○	○
	○	○	○
	○	○	○
	○	○	○
	○	○	○
	○	○	○
	○	○	○
	○	○	○
	○	○	○
	○	○	○

FEEDING

TIME	OUNCES

SLEEP

START TIME	END TIME

PLAY

○ reading & language

○ music/singing

○ art/crafts/motor skills

○ playtime with toys

○ outdoor time

○ other: _____

SUPPLIES NEEDED

MEDICATIONS

TIME	TYPE & AMOUNT

NOTES TO PARENT

MOOD

○ happy   ○ fussy

○ sleepy   ○ sick

○ quiet   ○ grumpy

○ other _____

_____

DATE: _____   ○ Mon ○ Tue ○ Wed ○ Thur ○ Fri ○ Sat ○ Sun

NOTES TO NANNY _____

| Wake Time | am | Last Fed At: | am |
| | pm | | pm |

DIAPERS

TIME	DRY	WET	DIRTY
	○	○	○
	○	○	○
	○	○	○
	○	○	○
	○	○	○
	○	○	○
	○	○	○
	○	○	○
	○	○	○
	○	○	○

FEEDING

TIME	OUNCES

SLEEP

START TIME	END TIME

PLAY

○ reading & language

○ music/singing

○ art/crafts/motor skills

○ playtime with toys

○ outdoor time

○ other: _____

SUPPLIES NEEDED

MEDICATIONS

TIME	TYPE & AMOUNT

NOTES TO PARENT

MOOD

○ happy   ○ fussy

○ sleepy   ○ sick

○ quiet   ○ grumpy

○ other   _____

DATE: _____   ○ Mon ○ Tue ○ Wed ○ Thur ○ Fri ○ Sat ○ Sun

NOTES TO NANNY _____

Wake Time	am	Last Fed At:	am
	pm		pm

DIAPERS

TIME	DRY	WET	DIRTY
	○	○	○
	○	○	○
	○	○	○
	○	○	○
	○	○	○
	○	○	○
	○	○	○
	○	○	○
	○	○	○
	○	○	○

FEEDING

TIME	OUNCES

SLEEP

START TIME	END TIME

PLAY

○ reading & language

○ music/singing

○ art/crafts/motor skills

○ playtime with toys

○ outdoor time

○ other: _____

SUPPLIES NEEDED

MEDICATIONS

TIME	TYPE & AMOUNT

NOTES TO PARENT

MOOD

○ happy   ○ fussy

○ sleepy   ○ sick

○ quiet   ○ grumpy

○ other _____

DATE: _____ ○ Mon ○ Tue ○ Wed ○ Thur ○ Fri ○ Sat ○ Sun

NOTES TO NANNY _____

Wake Time	am	Last Fed At:	am
	pm		pm

DIAPERS			
TIME	DRY	WET	DIRTY
	○	○	○
	○	○	○
	○	○	○
	○	○	○
	○	○	○
	○	○	○
	○	○	○
	○	○	○
	○	○	○
	○	○	○

FEEDING	
TIME	OUNCES

SLEEP	
START TIME	END TIME

PLAY

○ reading & language

○ music/singing

○ art/crafts/motor skills

○ playtime with toys

○ outdoor time

○ other: _____

SUPPLIES NEEDED

MEDICATIONS

TIME	TYPE & AMOUNT

NOTES TO PARENT

MOOD

○ happy   ○ fussy

○ sleepy   ○ sick

○ quiet   ○ grumpy

○ other _____

28

DATE: _____ ○ Mon ○ Tue ○ Wed ○ Thur ○ Fri ○ Sat ○ Sun

NOTES TO NANNY _____

Wake Time	am	Last Fed At:	am
	pm		pm

DIAPERS

TIME	DRY	WET	DIRTY
	○	○	○
	○	○	○
	○	○	○
	○	○	○
	○	○	○
	○	○	○
	○	○	○
	○	○	○
	○	○	○
	○	○	○

FEEDING

TIME	OUNCES

SLEEP

START TIME	END TIME

PLAY

○ reading & language

○ music/singing

○ art/crafts/motor skills

○ playtime with toys

○ outdoor time

○ other: _____

SUPPLIES NEEDED

MEDICATIONS

TIME	TYPE & AMOUNT

NOTES TO PARENT

MOOD

○ happy ○ fussy

○ sleepy ○ sick

○ quiet ○ grumpy

○ other _____

_____

DATE: _____ ○ Mon ○ Tue ○ Wed ○ Thur ○ Fri ○ Sat ○ Sun

NOTES TO NANNY _____

Wake Time	am	Last Fed At:	am
	pm		pm

DIAPERS			
TIME	DRY	WET	DIRTY
	○	○	○
	○	○	○
	○	○	○
	○	○	○
	○	○	○
	○	○	○
	○	○	○
	○	○	○
	○	○	○
	○	○	○

FEEDING	
TIME	OUNCES

SLEEP	
START TIME	END TIME

PLAY
○ reading & language
○ music/singing
○ art/crafts/motor skills
○ playtime with toys
○ outdoor time
○ other: _____

SUPPLIES NEEDED

MEDICATIONS	
TIME	TYPE & AMOUNT

NOTES TO PARENT

MOOD
○ happy ○ fussy
○ sleepy ○ sick
○ quiet ○ grumpy
○ other _____

DATE: _____   ◯ Mon ◯ Tue ◯ Wed ◯ Thur ◯ Fri ◯ Sat ◯ Sun

NOTES TO NANNY _____

_____

Wake Time	am	Last Fed At:	am
	pm		pm

DIAPERS

TIME	DRY	WET	DIRTY
	◯	◯	◯
	◯	◯	◯
	◯	◯	◯
	◯	◯	◯
	◯	◯	◯
	◯	◯	◯
	◯	◯	◯
	◯	◯	◯
	◯	◯	◯
	◯	◯	◯

FEEDING

TIME	OUNCES

SLEEP

START TIME	END TIME

PLAY

◯ reading & language

◯ music/singing

◯ art/crafts/motor skills

◯ playtime with toys

◯ outdoor time

◯ other: _____

SUPPLIES NEEDED

MEDICATIONS

TIME	TYPE & AMOUNT

NOTES TO PARENT

MOOD

◯ happy   ◯ fussy

◯ sleepy   ◯ sick

◯ quiet   ◯ grumpy

◯ other _____

_____

DATE: _____ ○ Mon ○ Tue ○ Wed ○ Thur ○ Fri ○ Sat ○ Sun

NOTES TO NANNY _____

| Wake Time | am | Last Fed At: | am |
| | pm | | pm |

DIAPERS			
TIME	DRY	WET	DIRTY
	○	○	○
	○	○	○
	○	○	○
	○	○	○
	○	○	○
	○	○	○
	○	○	○
	○	○	○
	○	○	○
	○	○	○

FEEDING	
TIME	OUNCES

SLEEP	
START TIME	END TIME

PLAY
○ reading & language
○ music/singing
○ art/crafts/motor skills
○ playtime with toys
○ outdoor time
○ other: _____

SUPPLIES NEEDED

MEDICATIONS	
TIME	TYPE & AMOUNT

NOTES TO PARENT

MOOD
○ happy   ○ fussy
○ sleepy   ○ sick
○ quiet   ○ grumpy
○ other _____

DATE: _____ ○ Mon ○ Tue ○ Wed ○ Thur ○ Fri ○ Sat ○ Sun

NOTES TO NANNY _____

| Wake Time | am | Last Fed At: | am |
| | pm | | pm |

DIAPERS			
TIME	DRY	WET	DIRTY
	○	○	○
	○	○	○
	○	○	○
	○	○	○
	○	○	○
	○	○	○
	○	○	○
	○	○	○
	○	○	○
	○	○	○

FEEDING	
TIME	OUNCES

SLEEP	
START TIME	END TIME

PLAY
○ reading & language
○ music/singing
○ art/crafts/motor skills
○ playtime with toys
○ outdoor time
○ other: _____

SUPPLIES NEEDED

MEDICATIONS	
TIME	TYPE & AMOUNT

NOTES TO PARENT

MOOD
○ happy   ○ fussy
○ sleepy   ○ sick
○ quiet   ○ grumpy
○ other _____

DATE: _____ ○ Mon ○ Tue ○ Wed ○ Thur ○ Fri ○ Sat ○ Sun

NOTES TO NANNY _____

_____

Wake Time	am	Last Fed At:	am
	pm		pm

DIAPERS

TIME	DRY	WET	DIRTY
	○	○	○
	○	○	○
	○	○	○
	○	○	○
	○	○	○
	○	○	○
	○	○	○
	○	○	○
	○	○	○
	○	○	○

FEEDING

TIME	OUNCES

SLEEP

START TIME	END TIME

PLAY

○ reading & language

○ music/singing

○ art/crafts/motor skills

○ playtime with toys

○ outdoor time

○ other: _____

SUPPLIES NEEDED

MEDICATIONS

TIME	TYPE & AMOUNT

NOTES TO PARENT

MOOD

○ happy   ○ fussy

○ sleepy   ○ sick

○ quiet   ○ grumpy

○ other _____

DATE: _____ ○ Mon ○ Tue ○ Wed ○ Thur ○ Fri ○ Sat ○ Sun

NOTES TO NANNY _____

Wake Time	am	Last Fed At:	am
	pm		pm

DIAPERS

TIME	DRY	WET	DIRTY
	○	○	○
	○	○	○
	○	○	○
	○	○	○
	○	○	○
	○	○	○
	○	○	○
	○	○	○
	○	○	○
	○	○	○

FEEDING

TIME	OUNCES

SLEEP

START TIME	END TIME

PLAY

○ reading & language

○ music/singing

○ art/crafts/motor skills

○ playtime with toys

○ outdoor time

○ other: _____

SUPPLIES NEEDED

MEDICATIONS

TIME	TYPE & AMOUNT

NOTES TO PARENT

MOOD

○ happy   ○ fussy

○ sleepy   ○ sick

○ quiet   ○ grumpy

○ other _____

DATE: _____   ○ Mon ○ Tue ○ Wed ○ Thur ○ Fri ○ Sat ○ Sun

NOTES TO NANNY _____

Wake Time	am	Last Fed At:	am
	pm		pm

DIAPERS

TIME	DRY	WET	DIRTY
	○	○	○
	○	○	○
	○	○	○
	○	○	○
	○	○	○
	○	○	○
	○	○	○
	○	○	○
	○	○	○
	○	○	○

FEEDING

TIME	OUNCES

SLEEP

START TIME	END TIME

PLAY

○ reading & language

○ music/singing

○ art/crafts/motor skills

○ playtime with toys

○ outdoor time

○ other: _____

SUPPLIES NEEDED

MEDICATIONS

TIME	TYPE & AMOUNT

NOTES TO PARENT

MOOD

○ happy   ○ fussy

○ sleepy   ○ sick

○ quiet   ○ grumpy

○ other _____

_____

DATE: _____   ○ Mon ○ Tue ○ Wed ○ Thur ○ Fri ○ Sat ○ Sun

NOTES TO NANNY _____

Wake Time	am	Last Fed At:	am
	pm		pm

DIAPERS

TIME	DRY	WET	DIRTY
	○	○	○
	○	○	○
	○	○	○
	○	○	○
	○	○	○
	○	○	○
	○	○	○
	○	○	○
	○	○	○
	○	○	○

FEEDING

TIME	OUNCES

SLEEP

START TIME	END TIME

PLAY

○ reading & language

○ music/singing

○ art/crafts/motor skills

○ playtime with toys

○ outdoor time

○ other: _____

SUPPLIES NEEDED

MEDICATIONS

TIME	TYPE & AMOUNT

NOTES TO PARENT

MOOD

○ happy   ○ fussy

○ sleepy   ○ sick

○ quiet   ○ grumpy

○ other _____

DATE: _____   ○ Mon ○ Tue ○ Wed ○ Thur ○ Fri ○ Sat ○ Sun

NOTES TO NANNY _____

_____

Wake Time	am	Last Fed At:	am
	pm		pm

DIAPERS

TIME	DRY	WET	DIRTY
	○	○	○
	○	○	○
	○	○	○
	○	○	○
	○	○	○
	○	○	○
	○	○	○
	○	○	○
	○	○	○
	○	○	○

FEEDING

TIME	OUNCES

SLEEP

START TIME	END TIME

PLAY

○ reading & language

○ music/singing

○ art/crafts/motor skills

○ playtime with toys

○ outdoor time

○ other: _____

SUPPLIES NEEDED

MEDICATIONS

TIME	TYPE & AMOUNT

NOTES TO PARENT

MOOD

○ happy   ○ fussy

○ sleepy   ○ sick

○ quiet   ○ grumpy

○ other _____

_____

DATE: _____ ○ Mon ○ Tue ○ Wed ○ Thur ○ Fri ○ Sat ○ Sun

NOTES TO NANNY _____

_____

_____

Wake Time	am	Last Fed At:	am
	pm		pm

DIAPERS

TIME	DRY	WET	DIRTY
	○	○	○
	○	○	○
	○	○	○
	○	○	○
	○	○	○
	○	○	○
	○	○	○
	○	○	○
	○	○	○
	○	○	○

FEEDING

TIME	OUNCES

SLEEP

START TIME	END TIME

PLAY

○ reading & language

○ music/singing

○ art/crafts/motor skills

○ playtime with toys

○ outdoor time

○ other: _____

SUPPLIES NEEDED

MEDICATIONS

TIME	TYPE & AMOUNT

NOTES TO PARENT

MOOD

○ happy   ○ fussy

○ sleepy   ○ sick

○ quiet   ○ grumpy

○ other _____

_____

DATE: _____   ○ Mon ○ Tue ○ Wed ○ Thur ○ Fri ○ Sat ○ Sun

NOTES TO NANNY _____

_____

Wake Time	am	Last Fed At:	am
	pm		pm

DIAPERS			
TIME	DRY	WET	DIRTY
	○	○	○
	○	○	○
	○	○	○
	○	○	○
	○	○	○
	○	○	○
	○	○	○
	○	○	○
	○	○	○
	○	○	○

FEEDING	
TIME	OUNCES

SLEEP	
START TIME	END TIME

PLAY
○ reading & language
○ music/singing
○ art/crafts/motor skills
○ playtime with toys
○ outdoor time
○ other: _____

SUPPLIES NEEDED

MEDICATIONS	
TIME	TYPE & AMOUNT

NOTES TO PARENT

MOOD	
○ happy	○ fussy
○ sleepy	○ sick
○ quiet	○ grumpy
○ other	_____

DATE: _____   ○ Mon ○ Tue ○ Wed ○ Thur ○ Fri ○ Sat ○ Sun

NOTES TO NANNY _____

_____

Wake Time	am	Last Fed At:	am
	pm		pm

DIAPERS			
TIME	DRY	WET	DIRTY
	○	○	○
	○	○	○
	○	○	○
	○	○	○
	○	○	○
	○	○	○
	○	○	○
	○	○	○
	○	○	○
	○	○	○

FEEDING	
TIME	OUNCES

SLEEP	
START TIME	END TIME

PLAY
○ reading & language
○ music/singing
○ art/crafts/motor skills
○ playtime with toys
○ outdoor time
○ other: _____

SUPPLIES NEEDED

MEDICATIONS	
TIME	TYPE & AMOUNT

NOTES TO PARENT

MOOD
○ happy ○ fussy
○ sleepy ○ sick
○ quiet ○ grumpy
○ other _____

DATE: _____   ○ Mon ○ Tue ○ Wed ○ Thur ○ Fri ○ Sat ○ Sun

NOTES TO NANNY _____

Wake Time	am	Last Fed At:	am
	pm		pm

DIAPERS

TIME	DRY	WET	DIRTY
	○	○	○
	○	○	○
	○	○	○
	○	○	○
	○	○	○
	○	○	○
	○	○	○
	○	○	○
	○	○	○
	○	○	○

FEEDING

TIME	OUNCES

SLEEP

START TIME	END TIME

PLAY

○ reading & language

○ music/singing

○ art/crafts/motor skills

○ playtime with toys

○ outdoor time

○ other: _____

SUPPLIES NEEDED

MEDICATIONS

TIME	TYPE & AMOUNT

NOTES TO PARENT

MOOD

○ happy   ○ fussy

○ sleepy   ○ sick

○ quiet   ○ grumpy

○ other   _____

DATE: _____   ○ Mon ○ Tue ○ Wed ○ Thur ○ Fri ○ Sat ○ Sun

NOTES TO NANNY _____

Wake Time	am	Last Fed At:	am
	pm		pm

DIAPERS			
TIME	DRY	WET	DIRTY
	○	○	○
	○	○	○
	○	○	○
	○	○	○
	○	○	○
	○	○	○
	○	○	○
	○	○	○
	○	○	○
	○	○	○

FEEDING	
TIME	OUNCES

SLEEP	
START TIME	END TIME

PLAY

○ reading & language

○ music/singing

○ art/crafts/motor skills

○ playtime with toys

○ outdoor time

○ other: _____

SUPPLIES NEEDED

MEDICATIONS	
TIME	TYPE & AMOUNT

NOTES TO PARENT

MOOD

○ happy   ○ fussy

○ sleepy   ○ sick

○ quiet   ○ grumpy

○ other _____

_____

DATE: _____   ○ Mon ○ Tue ○ Wed ○ Thur ○ Fri ○ Sat ○ Sun

NOTES TO NANNY _____

Wake Time	am	Last Fed At:	am
	pm		pm

DIAPERS

TIME	DRY	WET	DIRTY
	○	○	○
	○	○	○
	○	○	○
	○	○	○
	○	○	○
	○	○	○
	○	○	○
	○	○	○
	○	○	○
	○	○	○

FEEDING

TIME	OUNCES

SLEEP

START TIME	END TIME

PLAY

○ reading & language

○ music/singing

○ art/crafts/motor skills

○ playtime with toys

○ outdoor time

○ other: _____

SUPPLIES NEEDED

MEDICATIONS

TIME	TYPE & AMOUNT

NOTES TO PARENT

MOOD

○ happy   ○ fussy

○ sleepy   ○ sick

○ quiet   ○ grumpy

○ other _____

_____

DATE: _____   ○ Mon ○ Tue ○ Wed ○ Thur ○ Fri ○ Sat ○ Sun

NOTES TO NANNY _____

_____

Wake Time	am	Last Fed At:	am
	pm		pm

DIAPERS

TIME	DRY	WET	DIRTY
	○	○	○
	○	○	○
	○	○	○
	○	○	○
	○	○	○
	○	○	○
	○	○	○
	○	○	○
	○	○	○
	○	○	○

FEEDING

TIME	OUNCES

SLEEP

START TIME	END TIME

PLAY

○ reading & language

○ music/singing

○ art/crafts/motor skills

○ playtime with toys

○ outdoor time

○ other: _____

SUPPLIES NEEDED

MEDICATIONS

TIME	TYPE & AMOUNT

NOTES TO PARENT

MOOD

○ happy   ○ fussy

○ sleepy   ○ sick

○ quiet   ○ grumpy

○ other   _____

DATE: _____   ○ Mon ○ Tue ○ Wed ○ Thur ○ Fri ○ Sat ○ Sun

NOTES TO NANNY _____

Wake Time	am	Last Fed At:	am
	pm		pm

DIAPERS			
TIME	DRY	WET	DIRTY
	○	○	○
	○	○	○
	○	○	○
	○	○	○
	○	○	○
	○	○	○
	○	○	○
	○	○	○
	○	○	○
	○	○	○

FEEDING	
TIME	OUNCES

SLEEP	
START TIME	END TIME

PLAY

○ reading & language

○ music/singing

○ art/crafts/motor skills

○ playtime with toys

○ outdoor time

○ other: _____

SUPPLIES NEEDED

MEDICATIONS

TIME	TYPE & AMOUNT

NOTES TO PARENT

MOOD

○ happy   ○ fussy

○ sleepy   ○ sick

○ quiet   ○ grumpy

○ other _____

_____

46

DATE: _____ ○ Mon ○ Tue ○ Wed ○ Thur ○ Fri ○ Sat ○ Sun

NOTES TO NANNY _____

_____

Wake Time	am	Last Fed At:	am
	pm		pm

DIAPERS			
TIME	DRY	WET	DIRTY
	○	○	○
	○	○	○
	○	○	○
	○	○	○
	○	○	○
	○	○	○
	○	○	○
	○	○	○
	○	○	○
	○	○	○

FEEDING	
TIME	OUNCES

SLEEP	
START TIME	END TIME

PLAY

○ reading & language

○ music/singing

○ art/crafts/motor skills

○ playtime with toys

○ outdoor time

○ other: _____

SUPPLIES NEEDED

MEDICATIONS	
TIME	TYPE & AMOUNT

NOTES TO PARENT

MOOD

○ happy   ○ fussy

○ sleepy   ○ sick

○ quiet   ○ grumpy

○ other _____

_____

DATE: _____ ○ Mon ○ Tue ○ Wed ○ Thur ○ Fri ○ Sat ○ Sun

NOTES TO NANNY _____

Wake Time	am	Last Fed At:	am
	pm		pm

DIAPERS

TIME	DRY	WET	DIRTY
	○	○	○
	○	○	○
	○	○	○
	○	○	○
	○	○	○
	○	○	○
	○	○	○
	○	○	○
	○	○	○
	○	○	○

FEEDING

TIME	OUNCES

SLEEP

START TIME	END TIME

PLAY

○ reading & language

○ music/singing

○ art/crafts/motor skills

○ playtime with toys

○ outdoor time

○ other: _____

SUPPLIES NEEDED

MEDICATIONS

TIME	TYPE & AMOUNT

NOTES TO PARENT

MOOD

○ happy   ○ fussy

○ sleepy   ○ sick

○ quiet   ○ grumpy

○ other _____

_____

DATE: _____   ◯ Mon ◯ Tue ◯ Wed ◯ Thur ◯ Fri ◯ Sat ◯ Sun

NOTES TO NANNY _____
_____

Wake Time	am	Last Fed At:	am
	pm		pm

DIAPERS

TIME	DRY	WET	DIRTY
	◯	◯	◯
	◯	◯	◯
	◯	◯	◯
	◯	◯	◯
	◯	◯	◯
	◯	◯	◯
	◯	◯	◯
	◯	◯	◯
	◯	◯	◯
	◯	◯	◯

FEEDING

TIME	OUNCES

SLEEP

START TIME	END TIME

PLAY

◯ reading & language

◯ music/singing

◯ art/crafts/motor skills

◯ playtime with toys

◯ outdoor time

◯ other: _____

SUPPLIES NEEDED

MEDICATIONS

TIME	TYPE & AMOUNT

NOTES TO PARENT

MOOD

◯ happy   ◯ fussy

◯ sleepy   ◯ sick

◯ quiet   ◯ grumpy

◯ other _____

DATE: _____   ○ Mon ○ Tue ○ Wed ○ Thur ○ Fri ○ Sat ○ Sun

NOTES TO NANNY _____

Wake Time	am	Last Fed At:	am
	pm		pm

DIAPERS

TIME	DRY	WET	DIRTY
	○	○	○
	○	○	○
	○	○	○
	○	○	○
	○	○	○
	○	○	○
	○	○	○
	○	○	○
	○	○	○
	○	○	○

FEEDING

TIME	OUNCES

SLEEP

START TIME	END TIME

PLAY

○ reading & language

○ music/singing

○ art/crafts/motor skills

○ playtime with toys

○ outdoor time

○ other: _____

SUPPLIES NEEDED

MEDICATIONS

TIME	TYPE & AMOUNT

NOTES TO PARENT

MOOD

○ happy   ○ fussy

○ sleepy   ○ sick

○ quiet   ○ grumpy

○ other _____

DATE: _____   ◯ Mon ◯ Tue ◯ Wed ◯ Thur ◯ Fri ◯ Sat ◯ Sun

NOTES TO NANNY _____

Wake Time	am	Last Fed At:	am
	pm		pm

DIAPERS

TIME	DRY	WET	DIRTY
	◯	◯	◯
	◯	◯	◯
	◯	◯	◯
	◯	◯	◯
	◯	◯	◯
	◯	◯	◯
	◯	◯	◯
	◯	◯	◯
	◯	◯	◯
	◯	◯	◯

FEEDING

TIME	OUNCES

SLEEP

START TIME	END TIME

PLAY

◯ reading & language

◯ music/singing

◯ art/crafts/motor skills

◯ playtime with toys

◯ outdoor time

◯ other: _____

SUPPLIES NEEDED

MEDICATIONS

TIME	TYPE & AMOUNT

NOTES TO PARENT

MOOD

◯ happy   ◯ fussy

◯ sleepy ◯ sick

◯ quiet   ◯ grumpy

◯ other _____

DATE: _____ ○ Mon ○ Tue ○ Wed ○ Thur ○ Fri ○ Sat ○ Sun

NOTES TO NANNY _____

| Wake Time | am | Last Fed At: | am |
| | pm | | pm |

DIAPERS				FEEDING		SLEEP	
TIME	DRY	WET	DIRTY	TIME	OUNCES	START TIME	END TIME
	○	○	○				
	○	○	○				
	○	○	○				
	○	○	○				
	○	○	○				
	○	○	○				
	○	○	○				
	○	○	○				
	○	○	○				
	○	○	○				

PLAY

○ reading & language

○ music/singing

○ art/crafts/motor skills

○ playtime with toys

○ outdoor time

○ other: _____

SUPPLIES NEEDED

MEDICATIONS

TIME	TYPE & AMOUNT

NOTES TO PARENT

MOOD

○ happy   ○ fussy

○ sleepy   ○ sick

○ quiet   ○ grumpy

○ other _____

DATE: _____   ○ Mon ○ Tue ○ Wed ○ Thur ○ Fri ○ Sat ○ Sun

NOTES TO NANNY _____

Wake Time	am	Last Fed At:	am
	pm		pm

DIAPERS			
TIME	DRY	WET	DIRTY
	○	○	○
	○	○	○
	○	○	○
	○	○	○
	○	○	○
	○	○	○
	○	○	○
	○	○	○
	○	○	○
	○	○	○

FEEDING	
TIME	OUNCES

SLEEP	
START TIME	END TIME

PLAY
○ reading & language
○ music/singing
○ art/crafts/motor skills
○ playtime with toys
○ outdoor time
○ other: _____

SUPPLIES NEEDED

MEDICATIONS	
TIME	TYPE & AMOUNT

NOTES TO PARENT

MOOD	
○ happy	○ fussy
○ sleepy	○ sick
○ quiet	○ grumpy
○ other	_____

DATE: _____ ○ Mon ○ Tue ○ Wed ○ Thur ○ Fri ○ Sat ○ Sun

NOTES TO NANNY _____

Wake Time	am	Last Fed At:	am
	pm		pm

DIAPERS			
TIME	DRY	WET	DIRTY
	○	○	○
	○	○	○
	○	○	○
	○	○	○
	○	○	○
	○	○	○
	○	○	○
	○	○	○
	○	○	○
	○	○	○

FEEDING	
TIME	OUNCES

SLEEP	
START TIME	END TIME

PLAY
○ reading & language
○ music/singing
○ art/crafts/motor skills
○ playtime with toys
○ outdoor time
○ other: _____

SUPPLIES NEEDED

MEDICATIONS	
TIME	TYPE & AMOUNT

NOTES TO PARENT

MOOD
○ happy   ○ fussy
○ sleepy   ○ sick
○ quiet   ○ grumpy
○ other _____

DATE: _____   ○ Mon ○ Tue ○ Wed ○ Thur ○ Fri ○ Sat ○ Sun

NOTES TO NANNY _____

Wake Time	am	Last Fed At:	am
	pm		pm

DIAPERS

TIME	DRY	WET	DIRTY
	○	○	○
	○	○	○
	○	○	○
	○	○	○
	○	○	○
	○	○	○
	○	○	○
	○	○	○
	○	○	○
	○	○	○

FEEDING

TIME	OUNCES

SLEEP

START TIME	END TIME

PLAY

○ reading & language

○ music/singing

○ art/crafts/motor skills

○ playtime with toys

○ outdoor time

○ other: _____

SUPPLIES NEEDED

MEDICATIONS

TIME	TYPE & AMOUNT

NOTES TO PARENT

MOOD

○ happy   ○ fussy

○ sleepy   ○ sick

○ quiet   ○ grumpy

○ other _____

DATE: _____   ○ Mon ○ Tue ○ Wed ○ Thur ○ Fri ○ Sat ○ Sun

NOTES TO NANNY _____

Wake Time	am	Last Fed At:	am
	pm		pm

DIAPERS

TIME	DRY	WET	DIRTY
	○	○	○
	○	○	○
	○	○	○
	○	○	○
	○	○	○
	○	○	○
	○	○	○
	○	○	○
	○	○	○
	○	○	○

FEEDING

TIME	OUNCES

SLEEP

START TIME	END TIME

PLAY

○ reading & language

○ music/singing

○ art/crafts/motor skills

○ playtime with toys

○ outdoor time

○ other: _____

SUPPLIES NEEDED

MEDICATIONS

TIME	TYPE & AMOUNT

NOTES TO PARENT

MOOD

○ happy   ○ fussy

○ sleepy   ○ sick

○ quiet   ○ grumpy

○ other _____

DATE: _____ ○ Mon ○ Tue ○ Wed ○ Thur ○ Fri ○ Sat ○ Sun

NOTES TO NANNY _____

Wake Time	am	Last Fed At:	am
	pm		pm

DIAPERS			
TIME	DRY	WET	DIRTY
	○	○	○
	○	○	○
	○	○	○
	○	○	○
	○	○	○
	○	○	○
	○	○	○
	○	○	○
	○	○	○
	○	○	○

FEEDING	
TIME	OUNCES

SLEEP	
START TIME	END TIME

PLAY
○ reading & language
○ music/singing
○ art/crafts/motor skills
○ playtime with toys
○ outdoor time
○ other: _____

SUPPLIES NEEDED

MEDICATIONS	
TIME	TYPE & AMOUNT

NOTES TO PARENT

MOOD	
○ happy	○ fussy
○ sleepy	○ sick
○ quiet	○ grumpy
○ other	_____

DATE: _____ ○ Mon ○ Tue ○ Wed ○ Thur ○ Fri ○ Sat ○ Sun

NOTES TO NANNY _____

Wake Time	am	Last Fed At:	am
	pm		pm

DIAPERS			
TIME	DRY	WET	DIRTY
	○	○	○
	○	○	○
	○	○	○
	○	○	○
	○	○	○
	○	○	○
	○	○	○
	○	○	○
	○	○	○
	○	○	○

FEEDING	
TIME	OUNCES

SLEEP	
START TIME	END TIME

PLAY

○ reading & language

○ music/singing

○ art/crafts/motor skills

○ playtime with toys

○ outdoor time

○ other: _____

SUPPLIES NEEDED

MEDICATIONS

TIME	TYPE & AMOUNT

NOTES TO PARENT

MOOD

○ happy ○ fussy

○ sleepy ○ sick

○ quiet ○ grumpy

○ other _____

_____

DATE: _____ ○ Mon ○ Tue ○ Wed ○ Thur ○ Fri ○ Sat ○ Sun

NOTES TO NANNY _____

Wake Time	am	Last Fed At:	am
	pm		pm

DIAPERS

TIME	DRY	WET	DIRTY
	○	○	○
	○	○	○
	○	○	○
	○	○	○
	○	○	○
	○	○	○
	○	○	○
	○	○	○
	○	○	○
	○	○	○

FEEDING

TIME	OUNCES

SLEEP

START TIME	END TIME

PLAY

○ reading & language

○ music/singing

○ art/crafts/motor skills

○ playtime with toys

○ outdoor time

○ other: _____

SUPPLIES NEEDED

MEDICATIONS

TIME	TYPE & AMOUNT

NOTES TO PARENT

MOOD

○ happy   ○ fussy

○ sleepy   ○ sick

○ quiet   ○ grumpy

○ other _____

DATE: _____ ○ Mon ○ Tue ○ Wed ○ Thur ○ Fri ○ Sat ○ Sun

NOTES TO NANNY _____

Wake Time	am	Last Fed At:	am
	pm		pm

DIAPERS			
TIME	DRY	WET	DIRTY
	○	○	○
	○	○	○
	○	○	○
	○	○	○
	○	○	○
	○	○	○
	○	○	○
	○	○	○
	○	○	○
	○	○	○

FEEDING	
TIME	OUNCES

SLEEP	
START TIME	END TIME

PLAY

○ reading & language

○ music/singing

○ art/crafts/motor skills

○ playtime with toys

○ outdoor time

○ other: _____

SUPPLIES NEEDED

MEDICATIONS	
TIME	TYPE & AMOUNT

NOTES TO PARENT

MOOD

○ happy   ○ fussy

○ sleepy   ○ sick

○ quiet   ○ grumpy

○ other _____

DATE: _____ ○ Mon ○ Tue ○ Wed ○ Thur ○ Fri ○ Sat ○ Sun

NOTES TO NANNY _____

_____

_____

Wake Time	am	Last Fed At:	am
	pm		pm

DIAPERS			
TIME	DRY	WET	DIRTY
	○	○	○
	○	○	○
	○	○	○
	○	○	○
	○	○	○
	○	○	○
	○	○	○
	○	○	○
	○	○	○
	○	○	○

FEEDING	
TIME	OUNCES

SLEEP	
START TIME	END TIME

PLAY
○ reading & language
○ music/singing
○ art/crafts/motor skills
○ playtime with toys
○ outdoor time
○ other: _____

SUPPLIES NEEDED

MEDICATIONS	
TIME	TYPE & AMOUNT

NOTES TO PARENT

MOOD
○ happy ○ fussy
○ sleepy ○ sick
○ quiet ○ grumpy
○ other _____

DATE: _____   ○ Mon ○ Tue ○ Wed ○ Thur ○ Fri ○ Sat ○ Sun

NOTES TO NANNY _____

Wake Time	am	Last Fed At:	am
	pm		pm

DIAPERS

TIME	DRY	WET	DIRTY
	○	○	○
	○	○	○
	○	○	○
	○	○	○
	○	○	○
	○	○	○
	○	○	○
	○	○	○
	○	○	○
	○	○	○

FEEDING

TIME	OUNCES

SLEEP

START TIME	END TIME

PLAY

○ reading & language

○ music/singing

○ art/crafts/motor skills

○ playtime with toys

○ outdoor time

○ other: _____

SUPPLIES NEEDED

MEDICATIONS

TIME	TYPE & AMOUNT

NOTES TO PARENT

MOOD

○ happy   ○ fussy

○ sleepy   ○ sick

○ quiet   ○ grumpy

○ other _____

_____

62

DATE: _____   ○ Mon ○ Tue ○ Wed ○ Thur ○ Fri ○ Sat ○ Sun

NOTES TO NANNY _____

_____

Wake Time	am	Last Fed At:	am
	pm		pm

DIAPERS

TIME	DRY	WET	DIRTY
	○	○	○
	○	○	○
	○	○	○
	○	○	○
	○	○	○
	○	○	○
	○	○	○
	○	○	○
	○	○	○
	○	○	○

FEEDING

TIME	OUNCES

SLEEP

START TIME	END TIME

PLAY

○ reading & language

○ music/singing

○ art/crafts/motor skills

○ playtime with toys

○ outdoor time

○ other: _____

SUPPLIES NEEDED

MEDICATIONS

TIME	TYPE & AMOUNT

NOTES TO PARENT

MOOD

○ happy   ○ fussy

○ sleepy   ○ sick

○ quiet   ○ grumpy

○ other _____

_____

DATE: _____   ○ Mon ○ Tue ○ Wed ○ Thur ○ Fri ○ Sat ○ Sun

NOTES TO NANNY _____

Wake Time	am	Last Fed At:	am
	pm		pm

DIAPERS

TIME	DRY	WET	DIRTY
	○	○	○
	○	○	○
	○	○	○
	○	○	○
	○	○	○
	○	○	○
	○	○	○
	○	○	○
	○	○	○
	○	○	○

FEEDING

TIME	OUNCES

SLEEP

START TIME	END TIME

PLAY

○ reading & language

○ music/singing

○ art/crafts/motor skills

○ playtime with toys

○ outdoor time

○ other: _____

SUPPLIES NEEDED

MEDICATIONS

TIME	TYPE & AMOUNT

NOTES TO PARENT

MOOD

○ happy   ○ fussy

○ sleepy   ○ sick

○ quiet   ○ grumpy

○ other _____

64

DATE: _____   ○ Mon ○ Tue ○ Wed ○ Thur ○ Fri ○ Sat ○ Sun

NOTES TO NANNY _____

_____

Wake Time	am	Last Fed At:	am
	pm		pm

DIAPERS

TIME	DRY	WET	DIRTY
	○	○	○
	○	○	○
	○	○	○
	○	○	○
	○	○	○
	○	○	○
	○	○	○
	○	○	○
	○	○	○
	○	○	○

FEEDING

TIME	OUNCES

SLEEP

START TIME	END TIME

PLAY

○ reading & language

○ music/singing

○ art/crafts/motor skills

○ playtime with toys

○ outdoor time

○ other: _____

SUPPLIES NEEDED

MEDICATIONS

TIME	TYPE & AMOUNT

NOTES TO PARENT

MOOD

○ happy   ○ fussy

○ sleepy   ○ sick

○ quiet   ○ grumpy

○ other _____

_____

DATE: _____   ○ Mon ○ Tue ○ Wed ○ Thur ○ Fri ○ Sat ○ Sun

NOTES TO NANNY _____

Wake Time	am	Last Fed At:	am
	pm		pm

DIAPERS

TIME	DRY	WET	DIRTY
	○	○	○
	○	○	○
	○	○	○
	○	○	○
	○	○	○
	○	○	○
	○	○	○
	○	○	○
	○	○	○
	○	○	○

FEEDING

TIME	OUNCES

SLEEP

START TIME	END TIME

PLAY

○ reading & language

○ music/singing

○ art/crafts/motor skills

○ playtime with toys

○ outdoor time

○ other: _____

SUPPLIES NEEDED

MEDICATIONS

TIME	TYPE & AMOUNT

NOTES TO PARENT

MOOD

○ happy   ○ fussy

○ sleepy   ○ sick

○ quiet   ○ grumpy

○ other _____

DATE: _____   ○ Mon ○ Tue ○ Wed ○ Thur ○ Fri ○ Sat ○ Sun

NOTES TO NANNY _____

_____

Wake Time	am	Last Fed At:	am
	pm		pm

DIAPERS

TIME	DRY	WET	DIRTY
	○	○	○
	○	○	○
	○	○	○
	○	○	○
	○	○	○
	○	○	○
	○	○	○
	○	○	○
	○	○	○
	○	○	○

FEEDING

TIME	OUNCES

SLEEP

START TIME	END TIME

PLAY

○ reading & language

○ music/singing

○ art/crafts/motor skills

○ playtime with toys

○ outdoor time

○ other: _____

SUPPLIES NEEDED

MEDICATIONS

TIME	TYPE & AMOUNT

NOTES TO PARENT

MOOD

○ happy   ○ fussy

○ sleepy   ○ sick

○ quiet   ○ grumpy

○ other _____

DATE: _____   ○ Mon ○ Tue ○ Wed ○ Thur ○ Fri ○ Sat ○ Sun

NOTES TO NANNY _____

Wake Time	am	Last Fed At:	am
	pm		pm

DIAPERS

TIME	DRY	WET	DIRTY
	○	○	○
	○	○	○
	○	○	○
	○	○	○
	○	○	○
	○	○	○
	○	○	○
	○	○	○
	○	○	○
	○	○	○

FEEDING

TIME	OUNCES

SLEEP

START TIME	END TIME

PLAY

○ reading & language

○ music/singing

○ art/crafts/motor skills

○ playtime with toys

○ outdoor time

○ other: _____

SUPPLIES NEEDED

MEDICATIONS

TIME	TYPE & AMOUNT

NOTES TO PARENT

MOOD

○ happy   ○ fussy

○ sleepy   ○ sick

○ quiet   ○ grumpy

○ other _____

_____

DATE: _____   ○ Mon ○ Tue ○ Wed ○ Thur ○ Fri ○ Sat ○ Sun

NOTES TO NANNY _____

Wake Time	am	Last Fed At:	am
	pm		pm

DIAPERS

TIME	DRY	WET	DIRTY
	○	○	○
	○	○	○
	○	○	○
	○	○	○
	○	○	○
	○	○	○
	○	○	○
	○	○	○
	○	○	○
	○	○	○

FEEDING

TIME	OUNCES

SLEEP

START TIME	END TIME

PLAY

○ reading & language

○ music/singing

○ art/crafts/motor skills

○ playtime with toys

○ outdoor time

○ other: _____

SUPPLIES NEEDED

MEDICATIONS

TIME	TYPE & AMOUNT

NOTES TO PARENT

MOOD

○ happy   ○ fussy

○ sleepy   ○ sick

○ quiet   ○ grumpy

○ other   _____

_____

DATE: _____ ○ Mon ○ Tue ○ Wed ○ Thur ○ Fri ○ Sat ○ Sun

NOTES TO NANNY _____

| Wake Time | am | Last Fed At: | am |
| | pm | | pm |

DIAPERS

TIME	DRY	WET	DIRTY
	○	○	○
	○	○	○
	○	○	○
	○	○	○
	○	○	○
	○	○	○
	○	○	○
	○	○	○
	○	○	○
	○	○	○

FEEDING

TIME	OUNCES

SLEEP

START TIME	END TIME

PLAY

○ reading & language

○ music/singing

○ art/crafts/motor skills

○ playtime with toys

○ outdoor time

○ other: _____

SUPPLIES NEEDED

MEDICATIONS

TIME	TYPE & AMOUNT

NOTES TO PARENT

MOOD

○ happy   ○ fussy

○ sleepy   ○ sick

○ quiet   ○ grumpy

○ other _____

DATE: _____   ○ Mon ○ Tue ○ Wed ○ Thur ○ Fri ○ Sat ○ Sun

NOTES TO NANNY _____

| Wake Time | am | Last Fed At: | am |
| | pm | | pm |

DIAPERS

TIME	DRY	WET	DIRTY
	○	○	○
	○	○	○
	○	○	○
	○	○	○
	○	○	○
	○	○	○
	○	○	○
	○	○	○
	○	○	○
	○	○	○

FEEDING

TIME	OUNCES

SLEEP

START TIME	END TIME

PLAY

○ reading & language

○ music/singing

○ art/crafts/motor skills

○ playtime with toys

○ outdoor time

○ other: _____

SUPPLIES NEEDED

MEDICATIONS

TIME	TYPE & AMOUNT

NOTES TO PARENT

MOOD

○ happy   ○ fussy

○ sleepy   ○ sick

○ quiet   ○ grumpy

○ other _____

DATE: _____   ○ Mon ○ Tue ○ Wed ○ Thur ○ Fri ○ Sat ○ Sun

NOTES TO NANNY _____

| Wake Time | am | Last Fed At: | am |
| | pm | | pm |

DIAPERS			
TIME	DRY	WET	DIRTY
	○	○	○
	○	○	○
	○	○	○
	○	○	○
	○	○	○
	○	○	○
	○	○	○
	○	○	○
	○	○	○
	○	○	○

FEEDING	
TIME	OUNCES

SLEEP	
START TIME	END TIME

PLAY
○ reading & language
○ music/singing
○ art/crafts/motor skills
○ playtime with toys
○ outdoor time
○ other: _____

SUPPLIES NEEDED

MEDICATIONS	
TIME	TYPE & AMOUNT

NOTES TO PARENT

MOOD	
○ happy	○ fussy
○ sleepy	○ sick
○ quiet	○ grumpy
○ other	_____

DATE: _____   ○ Mon ○ Tue ○ Wed ○ Thur ○ Fri ○ Sat ○ Sun

NOTES TO NANNY _____

Wake Time	am	Last Fed At:	am
	pm		pm

DIAPERS			
TIME	DRY	WET	DIRTY
	○	○	○
	○	○	○
	○	○	○
	○	○	○
	○	○	○
	○	○	○
	○	○	○
	○	○	○
	○	○	○
	○	○	○

FEEDING	
TIME	OUNCES

SLEEP	
START TIME	END TIME

PLAY

○ reading & language

○ music/singing

○ art/crafts/motor skills

○ playtime with toys

○ outdoor time

○ other: _____

SUPPLIES NEEDED

MEDICATIONS	
TIME	TYPE & AMOUNT

NOTES TO PARENT

MOOD

○ happy   ○ fussy

○ sleepy   ○ sick

○ quiet   ○ grumpy

○ other _____

_____

DATE: _____   ○ Mon ○ Tue ○ Wed ○ Thur ○ Fri ○ Sat ○ Sun

NOTES TO NANNY _____
_____

Wake Time	am	Last Fed At:	am
	pm		pm

DIAPERS			
TIME	DRY	WET	DIRTY
	○	○	○
	○	○	○
	○	○	○
	○	○	○
	○	○	○
	○	○	○
	○	○	○
	○	○	○
	○	○	○
	○	○	○

FEEDING	
TIME	OUNCES

SLEEP	
START TIME	END TIME

PLAY

○ reading & language

○ music/singing

○ art/crafts/motor skills

○ playtime with toys

○ outdoor time

○ other: _____

SUPPLIES NEEDED

MEDICATIONS	
TIME	TYPE & AMOUNT

NOTES TO PARENT

MOOD

○ happy   ○ fussy

○ sleepy   ○ sick

○ quiet   ○ grumpy

○ other   _____

DATE: _____ ○ Mon ○ Tue ○ Wed ○ Thur ○ Fri ○ Sat ○ Sun

NOTES TO NANNY _____

	Wake Time	am	Last Fed At:	am
		pm		pm

DIAPERS			
TIME	DRY	WET	DIRTY
	○	○	○
	○	○	○
	○	○	○
	○	○	○
	○	○	○
	○	○	○
	○	○	○
	○	○	○
	○	○	○
	○	○	○

FEEDING	
TIME	OUNCES

SLEEP	
START TIME	END TIME

PLAY
○ reading & language
○ music/singing
○ art/crafts/motor skills
○ playtime with toys
○ outdoor time
○ other: _____

SUPPLIES NEEDED

MEDICATIONS	
TIME	TYPE & AMOUNT

NOTES TO PARENT

MOOD	
○ happy	○ fussy
○ sleepy	○ sick
○ quiet	○ grumpy
○ other	_____

DATE: _____   ○ Mon ○ Tue ○ Wed ○ Thur ○ Fri ○ Sat ○ Sun

NOTES TO NANNY _____
_____

Wake Time	am	Last Fed At:	am
	pm		pm

DIAPERS

TIME	DRY	WET	DIRTY
	○	○	○
	○	○	○
	○	○	○
	○	○	○
	○	○	○
	○	○	○
	○	○	○
	○	○	○
	○	○	○
	○	○	○

FEEDING

TIME	OUNCES

SLEEP

START TIME	END TIME

PLAY

○ reading & language
○ music/singing
○ art/crafts/motor skills
○ playtime with toys
○ outdoor time
○ other: _____

SUPPLIES NEEDED

MEDICATIONS

TIME	TYPE & AMOUNT

NOTES TO PARENT

MOOD

○ happy   ○ fussy
○ sleepy   ○ sick
○ quiet   ○ grumpy
○ other _____

DATE: _____   ○ Mon ○ Tue ○ Wed ○ Thur ○ Fri ○ Sat ○ Sun

NOTES TO NANNY _____
_____

Wake Time	am	Last Fed At:	am
	pm		pm

DIAPERS

TIME	DRY	WET	DIRTY
	○	○	○
	○	○	○
	○	○	○
	○	○	○
	○	○	○
	○	○	○
	○	○	○
	○	○	○
	○	○	○
	○	○	○

FEEDING

TIME	OUNCES

SLEEP

START TIME	END TIME

PLAY

○ reading & language

○ music/singing

○ art/crafts/motor skills

○ playtime with toys

○ outdoor time

○ other: _____

SUPPLIES NEEDED

MEDICATIONS

TIME	TYPE & AMOUNT

NOTES TO PARENT

MOOD

○ happy   ○ fussy

○ sleepy   ○ sick

○ quiet   ○ grumpy

○ other _____

DATE: _____   ○ Mon ○ Tue ○ Wed ○ Thur ○ Fri ○ Sat ○ Sun

NOTES TO NANNY _____

| Wake Time | am | Last Fed At: | am |
| | pm | | pm |

DIAPERS

TIME	DRY	WET	DIRTY
	○	○	○
	○	○	○
	○	○	○
	○	○	○
	○	○	○
	○	○	○
	○	○	○
	○	○	○
	○	○	○
	○	○	○

FEEDING

TIME	OUNCES

SLEEP

START TIME	END TIME

PLAY

○ reading & language

○ music/singing

○ art/crafts/motor skills

○ playtime with toys

○ outdoor time

○ other: _____

SUPPLIES NEEDED

MEDICATIONS

TIME	TYPE & AMOUNT

NOTES TO PARENT

MOOD

○ happy   ○ fussy

○ sleepy   ○ sick

○ quiet   ○ grumpy

○ other _____

78

DATE: _____ ○ Mon ○ Tue ○ Wed ○ Thur ○ Fri ○ Sat ○ Sun

NOTES TO NANNY _____
_____
_____

Wake Time	am	Last Fed At:	am
	pm		pm

DIAPERS

TIME	DRY	WET	DIRTY
	○	○	○
	○	○	○
	○	○	○
	○	○	○
	○	○	○
	○	○	○
	○	○	○
	○	○	○
	○	○	○
	○	○	○

FEEDING

TIME	OUNCES

SLEEP

START TIME	END TIME

PLAY

○ reading & language

○ music/singing

○ art/crafts/motor skills

○ playtime with toys

○ outdoor time

○ other: _____

SUPPLIES NEEDED

MEDICATIONS

TIME	TYPE & AMOUNT

NOTES TO PARENT

MOOD

○ happy   ○ fussy

○ sleepy   ○ sick

○ quiet   ○ grumpy

○ other _____

DATE: _____   ○ Mon ○ Tue ○ Wed ○ Thur ○ Fri ○ Sat ○ Sun

NOTES TO NANNY _____

Wake Time	am	Last Fed At:	am
	pm		pm

DIAPERS

TIME	DRY	WET	DIRTY
	○	○	○
	○	○	○
	○	○	○
	○	○	○
	○	○	○
	○	○	○
	○	○	○
	○	○	○
	○	○	○
	○	○	○

FEEDING

TIME	OUNCES

SLEEP

START TIME	END TIME

PLAY

○ reading & language

○ music/singing

○ art/crafts/motor skills

○ playtime with toys

○ outdoor time

○ other: _____

SUPPLIES NEEDED

MEDICATIONS

TIME	TYPE & AMOUNT

NOTES TO PARENT

MOOD

○ happy   ○ fussy

○ sleepy   ○ sick

○ quiet   ○ grumpy

○ other _____

DATE: _____   ○ Mon ○ Tue ○ Wed ○ Thur ○ Fri ○ Sat ○ Sun

NOTES TO NANNY _____

Wake Time	am	Last Fed At:	am
	pm		pm

DIAPERS

TIME	DRY	WET	DIRTY
	○	○	○
	○	○	○
	○	○	○
	○	○	○
	○	○	○
	○	○	○
	○	○	○
	○	○	○
	○	○	○
	○	○	○

FEEDING

TIME	OUNCES

SLEEP

START TIME	END TIME

PLAY

○ reading & language

○ music/singing

○ art/crafts/motor skills

○ playtime with toys

○ outdoor time

○ other: _____

SUPPLIES NEEDED

MEDICATIONS

TIME	TYPE & AMOUNT

NOTES TO PARENT

MOOD

○ happy   ○ fussy

○ sleepy   ○ sick

○ quiet   ○ grumpy

○ other _____

81

DATE: _____   ○ Mon ○ Tue ○ Wed ○ Thur ○ Fri ○ Sat ○ Sun

NOTES TO NANNY _____

Wake Time	am	Last Fed At:	am
	pm		pm

DIAPERS

TIME	DRY	WET	DIRTY
	○	○	○
	○	○	○
	○	○	○
	○	○	○
	○	○	○
	○	○	○
	○	○	○
	○	○	○
	○	○	○
	○	○	○

FEEDING

TIME	OUNCES

SLEEP

START TIME	END TIME

PLAY

○ reading & language

○ music/singing

○ art/crafts/motor skills

○ playtime with toys

○ outdoor time

○ other: _____

SUPPLIES NEEDED

MEDICATIONS

TIME	TYPE & AMOUNT

NOTES TO PARENT

MOOD

○ happy   ○ fussy

○ sleepy   ○ sick

○ quiet   ○ grumpy

○ other _____

DATE: _____   ○ Mon ○ Tue ○ Wed ○ Thur ○ Fri ○ Sat ○ Sun

NOTES TO NANNY _____
_____

| Wake Time | am | Last Fed At: | am |
| | pm | | pm |

DIAPERS

TIME	DRY	WET	DIRTY
	○	○	○
	○	○	○
	○	○	○
	○	○	○
	○	○	○
	○	○	○
	○	○	○
	○	○	○
	○	○	○
	○	○	○

FEEDING

TIME	OUNCES

SLEEP

START TIME	END TIME

PLAY

○ reading & language
○ music/singing
○ art/crafts/motor skills
○ playtime with toys
○ outdoor time
○ other: _____

SUPPLIES NEEDED

MEDICATIONS

TIME	TYPE & AMOUNT

NOTES TO PARENT

MOOD

○ happy   ○ fussy
○ sleepy   ○ sick
○ quiet   ○ grumpy
○ other _____
_____

DATE: _____   ○ Mon ○ Tue ○ Wed ○ Thur ○ Fri ○ Sat ○ Sun

NOTES TO NANNY _____

Wake Time	am	Last Fed At:	am
	pm		pm

DIAPERS

TIME	DRY	WET	DIRTY
	○	○	○
	○	○	○
	○	○	○
	○	○	○
	○	○	○
	○	○	○
	○	○	○
	○	○	○
	○	○	○
	○	○	○

FEEDING

TIME	OUNCES

SLEEP

START TIME	END TIME

PLAY

○ reading & language

○ music/singing

○ art/crafts/motor skills

○ playtime with toys

○ outdoor time

○ other: _____

SUPPLIES NEEDED

MEDICATIONS

TIME	TYPE & AMOUNT

NOTES TO PARENT

MOOD

○ happy   ○ fussy

○ sleepy   ○ sick

○ quiet   ○ grumpy

○ other _____

DATE: _____ ○ Mon ○ Tue ○ Wed ○ Thur ○ Fri ○ Sat ○ Sun

NOTES TO NANNY _____

Wake Time	am	Last Fed At:	am
	pm		pm

DIAPERS			
TIME	DRY	WET	DIRTY
	○	○	○
	○	○	○
	○	○	○
	○	○	○
	○	○	○
	○	○	○
	○	○	○
	○	○	○
	○	○	○
	○	○	○

FEEDING	
TIME	OUNCES

SLEEP	
START TIME	END TIME

PLAY
○ reading & language
○ music/singing
○ art/crafts/motor skills
○ playtime with toys
○ outdoor time
○ other: _____

SUPPLIES NEEDED

MEDICATIONS	
TIME	TYPE & AMOUNT

NOTES TO PARENT

MOOD
○ happy   ○ fussy
○ sleepy   ○ sick
○ quiet   ○ grumpy
○ other _____

DATE: _____   ○ Mon ○ Tue ○ Wed ○ Thur ○ Fri ○ Sat ○ Sun

NOTES TO NANNY _____

_____

Wake Time	am	Last Fed At:	am
	pm		pm

DIAPERS

TIME	DRY	WET	DIRTY
	○	○	○
	○	○	○
	○	○	○
	○	○	○
	○	○	○
	○	○	○
	○	○	○
	○	○	○
	○	○	○
	○	○	○

FEEDING

TIME	OUNCES

SLEEP

START TIME	END TIME

PLAY

○ reading & language

○ music/singing

○ art/crafts/motor skills

○ playtime with toys

○ outdoor time

○ other: _____

SUPPLIES NEEDED

MEDICATIONS

TIME	TYPE & AMOUNT

NOTES TO PARENT

MOOD

○ happy   ○ fussy

○ sleepy   ○ sick

○ quiet   ○ grumpy

○ other   _____

_____

86

DATE: _____ ○ Mon ○ Tue ○ Wed ○ Thur ○ Fri ○ Sat ○ Sun

NOTES TO NANNY _____

_____

_____

Wake Time	am	Last Fed At:	am
	pm		pm

DIAPERS

TIME	DRY	WET	DIRTY
	○	○	○
	○	○	○
	○	○	○
	○	○	○
	○	○	○
	○	○	○
	○	○	○
	○	○	○
	○	○	○

FEEDING

TIME	OUNCES

SLEEP

START TIME	END TIME

PLAY

○ reading & language

○ music/singing

○ art/crafts/motor skills

○ playtime with toys

○ outdoor time

○ other: _____

SUPPLIES NEEDED

MEDICATIONS

TIME	TYPE & AMOUNT

NOTES TO PARENT

MOOD

○ happy   ○ fussy

○ sleepy   ○ sick

○ quiet   ○ grumpy

○ other _____

87

DATE: _____   ○ Mon ○ Tue ○ Wed ○ Thur ○ Fri ○ Sat ○ Sun

NOTES TO NANNY _____

Wake Time	am	Last Fed At:	am
	pm		pm

DIAPERS

TIME	DRY	WET	DIRTY
	○	○	○
	○	○	○
	○	○	○
	○	○	○
	○	○	○
	○	○	○
	○	○	○
	○	○	○
	○	○	○
	○	○	○

FEEDING

TIME	OUNCES

SLEEP

START TIME	END TIME

PLAY

○ reading & language

○ music/singing

○ art/crafts/motor skills

○ playtime with toys

○ outdoor time

○ other: _____

SUPPLIES NEEDED

MEDICATIONS

TIME	TYPE & AMOUNT

NOTES TO PARENT

MOOD

○ happy   ○ fussy

○ sleepy   ○ sick

○ quiet   ○ grumpy

○ other _____

DATE: _____ ○ Mon ○ Tue ○ Wed ○ Thur ○ Fri ○ Sat ○ Sun

NOTES TO NANNY _____

| Wake Time | am | Last Fed At: | am |
| | pm | | pm |

DIAPERS

TIME	DRY	WET	DIRTY
	○	○	○
	○	○	○
	○	○	○
	○	○	○
	○	○	○
	○	○	○
	○	○	○
	○	○	○
	○	○	○
	○	○	○

FEEDING

TIME	OUNCES

SLEEP

START TIME	END TIME

PLAY

○ reading & language

○ music/singing

○ art/crafts/motor skills

○ playtime with toys

○ outdoor time

○ other: _____

SUPPLIES NEEDED

MEDICATIONS

TIME	TYPE & AMOUNT

NOTES TO PARENT

MOOD

○ happy   ○ fussy

○ sleepy   ○ sick

○ quiet   ○ grumpy

○ other _____

DATE: _____   ○ Mon ○ Tue ○ Wed ○ Thur ○ Fri ○ Sat ○ Sun

NOTES TO NANNY _____

Wake Time	am	Last Fed At:	am
	pm		pm

DIAPERS

TIME	DRY	WET	DIRTY
	○	○	○
	○	○	○
	○	○	○
	○	○	○
	○	○	○
	○	○	○
	○	○	○
	○	○	○
	○	○	○
	○	○	○

FEEDING

TIME	OUNCES

SLEEP

START TIME	END TIME

PLAY

○ reading & language

○ music/singing

○ art/crafts/motor skills

○ playtime with toys

○ outdoor time

○ other: _____

SUPPLIES NEEDED

MEDICATIONS

TIME	TYPE & AMOUNT

NOTES TO PARENT

MOOD

○ happy   ○ fussy

○ sleepy   ○ sick

○ quiet   ○ grumpy

○ other _____

90

DATE: _____   ○ Mon ○ Tue ○ Wed ○ Thur ○ Fri ○ Sat ○ Sun

NOTES TO NANNY _____

_____

Wake Time	am	Last Fed At:	am
	pm		pm

DIAPERS			
TIME	DRY	WET	DIRTY
	○	○	○
	○	○	○
	○	○	○
	○	○	○
	○	○	○
	○	○	○
	○	○	○
	○	○	○
	○	○	○
	○	○	○

FEEDING	
TIME	OUNCES

SLEEP	
START TIME	END TIME

PLAY
○ reading & language
○ music/singing
○ art/crafts/motor skills
○ playtime with toys
○ outdoor time
○ other: _____

SUPPLIES NEEDED

MEDICATIONS	
TIME	TYPE & AMOUNT

NOTES TO PARENT

MOOD
○ happy   ○ fussy
○ sleepy   ○ sick
○ quiet   ○ grumpy
○ other _____
_____

DATE: _____ ○ Mon ○ Tue ○ Wed ○ Thur ○ Fri ○ Sat ○ Sun

NOTES TO NANNY _____

Wake Time	am	Last Fed At:	am
	pm		pm

DIAPERS

TIME	DRY	WET	DIRTY
	○	○	○
	○	○	○
	○	○	○
	○	○	○
	○	○	○
	○	○	○
	○	○	○
	○	○	○
	○	○	○
	○	○	○

FEEDING

TIME	OUNCES

SLEEP

START TIME	END TIME

PLAY

○ reading & language

○ music/singing

○ art/crafts/motor skills

○ playtime with toys

○ outdoor time

○ other: _____

SUPPLIES NEEDED

MEDICATIONS

TIME	TYPE & AMOUNT

NOTES TO PARENT

MOOD

○ happy   ○ fussy

○ sleepy   ○ sick

○ quiet   ○ grumpy

○ other _____

92

DATE: _____ ○ Mon ○ Tue ○ Wed ○ Thur ○ Fri ○ Sat ○ Sun

NOTES TO NANNY _____
_____

| Wake Time | am | Last Fed At: | am |
| | pm | | pm |

DIAPERS

TIME	DRY	WET	DIRTY
	○	○	○
	○	○	○
	○	○	○
	○	○	○
	○	○	○
	○	○	○
	○	○	○
	○	○	○
	○	○	○
	○	○	○
	○	○	○

FEEDING

TIME	OUNCES

SLEEP

START TIME	END TIME

PLAY

○ reading & language

○ music/singing

○ art/crafts/motor skills

○ playtime with toys

○ outdoor time

○ other: _____

SUPPLIES NEEDED

MEDICATIONS

TIME	TYPE & AMOUNT

NOTES TO PARENT

MOOD

○ happy   ○ fussy

○ sleepy   ○ sick

○ quiet   ○ grumpy

○ other _____

_____

DATE: _____ ○ Mon ○ Tue ○ Wed ○ Thur ○ Fri ○ Sat ○ Sun

NOTES TO NANNY _____

Wake Time	am	Last Fed At:	am
	pm		pm

DIAPERS			
TIME	DRY	WET	DIRTY
	○	○	○
	○	○	○
	○	○	○
	○	○	○
	○	○	○
	○	○	○
	○	○	○
	○	○	○
	○	○	○
	○	○	○

FEEDING	
TIME	OUNCES

SLEEP	
START TIME	END TIME

PLAY
○ reading & language
○ music/singing
○ art/crafts/motor skills
○ playtime with toys
○ outdoor time
○ other:

SUPPLIES NEEDED

MEDICATIONS	
TIME	TYPE & AMOUNT

NOTES TO PARENT

MOOD	
○ happy	○ fussy
○ sleepy	○ sick
○ quiet	○ grumpy
○ other	_____

DATE: _____   ◯ Mon ◯ Tue ◯ Wed ◯ Thur ◯ Fri ◯ Sat ◯ Sun

NOTES TO NANNY _____

_____

Wake Time	am	Last Fed At:	am
	pm		pm

DIAPERS

TIME	DRY	WET	DIRTY
	◯	◯	◯
	◯	◯	◯
	◯	◯	◯
	◯	◯	◯
	◯	◯	◯
	◯	◯	◯
	◯	◯	◯
	◯	◯	◯
	◯	◯	◯
	◯	◯	◯

FEEDING

TIME	OUNCES

SLEEP

START TIME	END TIME

PLAY

◯ reading & language

◯ music/singing

◯ art/crafts/motor skills

◯ playtime with toys

◯ outdoor time

◯ other: _____

SUPPLIES NEEDED

MEDICATIONS

TIME	TYPE & AMOUNT

NOTES TO PARENT

MOOD

◯ happy   ◯ fussy

◯ sleepy   ◯ sick

◯ quiet   ◯ grumpy

◯ other

_____

DATE: _____   ○ Mon ○ Tue ○ Wed ○ Thur ○ Fri ○ Sat ○ Sun

NOTES TO NANNY _____

Wake Time	am	Last Fed At:	am
	pm		pm

DIAPERS			
TIME	DRY	WET	DIRTY
	○	○	○
	○	○	○
	○	○	○
	○	○	○
	○	○	○
	○	○	○
	○	○	○
	○	○	○
	○	○	○
	○	○	○

FEEDING	
TIME	OUNCES

SLEEP	
START TIME	END TIME

PLAY
○ reading & language
○ music/singing
○ art/crafts/motor skills
○ playtime with toys
○ outdoor time
○ other: _____

SUPPLIES NEEDED

MEDICATIONS	
TIME	TYPE & AMOUNT

NOTES TO PARENT

MOOD
○ happy ○ fussy
○ sleepy ○ sick
○ quiet ○ grumpy
○ other _____

DATE: _____   ○ Mon ○ Tue ○ Wed ○ Thur ○ Fri ○ Sat ○ Sun

NOTES TO NANNY _____

_____

_____

Wake Time	am	Last Fed At:	am
	pm		pm

DIAPERS

TIME	DRY	WET	DIRTY
	○	○	○
	○	○	○
	○	○	○
	○	○	○
	○	○	○
	○	○	○
	○	○	○
	○	○	○
	○	○	○
	○	○	○

FEEDING

TIME	OUNCES

SLEEP

START TIME	END TIME

PLAY

○ reading & language

○ music/singing

○ art/crafts/motor skills

○ playtime with toys

○ outdoor time

○ other:

SUPPLIES NEEDED

MEDICATIONS

TIME	TYPE & AMOUNT

NOTES TO PARENT

MOOD

○ happy   ○ fussy

○ sleepy   ○ sick

○ quiet   ○ grumpy

○ other _____

_____

DATE: _____   ○ Mon ○ Tue ○ Wed ○ Thur ○ Fri ○ Sat ○ Sun

NOTES TO NANNY _____

	Wake Time	am	Last Fed At:	am
		pm		pm

DIAPERS

TIME	DRY	WET	DIRTY
	○	○	○
	○	○	○
	○	○	○
	○	○	○
	○	○	○
	○	○	○
	○	○	○
	○	○	○
	○	○	○
	○	○	○

FEEDING

TIME	OUNCES

SLEEP

START TIME	END TIME

PLAY

○ reading & language

○ music/singing

○ art/crafts/motor skills

○ playtime with toys

○ outdoor time

○ other: _____

SUPPLIES NEEDED

MEDICATIONS

TIME	TYPE & AMOUNT

NOTES TO PARENT

MOOD

○ happy   ○ fussy

○ sleepy   ○ sick

○ quiet   ○ grumpy

○ other _____

DATE: _____   ○ Mon ○ Tue ○ Wed ○ Thur ○ Fri ○ Sat ○ Sun

NOTES TO NANNY _____

_____

| Wake Time | am | Last Fed At: | am |
| | pm | | pm |

DIAPERS

TIME	DRY	WET	DIRTY
	○	○	○
	○	○	○
	○	○	○
	○	○	○
	○	○	○
	○	○	○
	○	○	○
	○	○	○
	○	○	○
	○	○	○

FEEDING

TIME	OUNCES

SLEEP

START TIME	END TIME

PLAY

○ reading & language

○ music/singing

○ art/crafts/motor skills

○ playtime with toys

○ outdoor time

○ other: _____

SUPPLIES NEEDED

MEDICATIONS

TIME	TYPE & AMOUNT

NOTES TO PARENT

MOOD

○ happy   ○ fussy

○ sleepy   ○ sick

○ quiet   ○ grumpy

○ other _____

99

DATE: _____ ○ Mon ○ Tue ○ Wed ○ Thur ○ Fri ○ Sat ○ Sun

NOTES TO NANNY _____

| Wake Time | am | Last Fed At: | am |
| | pm | | pm |

DIAPERS

TIME	DRY	WET	DIRTY
	○	○	○
	○	○	○
	○	○	○
	○	○	○
	○	○	○
	○	○	○
	○	○	○
	○	○	○
	○	○	○
	○	○	○

FEEDING

TIME	OUNCES

SLEEP

START TIME	END TIME

PLAY

○ reading & language

○ music/singing

○ art/crafts/motor skills

○ playtime with toys

○ outdoor time

○ other: _____

SUPPLIES NEEDED

MEDICATIONS

TIME	TYPE & AMOUNT

NOTES TO PARENT

MOOD

○ happy   ○ fussy

○ sleepy   ○ sick

○ quiet   ○ grumpy

○ other _____

DATE: _____ ○ Mon ○ Tue ○ Wed ○ Thur ○ Fri ○ Sat ○ Sun

NOTES TO NANNY _____

_____

| Wake Time | am | Last Fed At: | am |
| | pm | | pm |

DIAPERS

TIME	DRY	WET	DIRTY
	○	○	○
	○	○	○
	○	○	○
	○	○	○
	○	○	○
	○	○	○
	○	○	○
	○	○	○
	○	○	○
	○	○	○

FEEDING

TIME	OUNCES

SLEEP

START TIME	END TIME

PLAY

○ reading & language

○ music/singing

○ art/crafts/motor skills

○ playtime with toys

○ outdoor time

○ other: _____

SUPPLIES NEEDED

MEDICATIONS

TIME	TYPE & AMOUNT

NOTES TO PARENT

MOOD

○ happy   ○ fussy

○ sleepy   ○ sick

○ quiet   ○ grumpy

○ other   _____

_____

DATE: _____ ○ Mon ○ Tue ○ Wed ○ Thur ○ Fri ○ Sat ○ Sun

NOTES TO NANNY _____

_____

Wake Time	am	Last Fed At:	am
	pm		pm

DIAPERS

TIME	DRY	WET	DIRTY
	○	○	○
	○	○	○
	○	○	○
	○	○	○
	○	○	○
	○	○	○
	○	○	○
	○	○	○
	○	○	○
	○	○	○

FEEDING

TIME	OUNCES

SLEEP

START TIME	END TIME

PLAY

○ reading & language

○ music/singing

○ art/crafts/motor skills

○ playtime with toys

○ outdoor time

○ other: _____

SUPPLIES NEEDED

MEDICATIONS

TIME	TYPE & AMOUNT

NOTES TO PARENT

MOOD

○ happy ○ fussy

○ sleepy ○ sick

○ quiet ○ grumpy

○ other _____

DATE: _____ ○ Mon ○ Tue ○ Wed ○ Thur ○ Fri ○ Sat ○ Sun

NOTES TO NANNY _____

_____

Wake Time	am	Last Fed At:	am
	pm		pm

DIAPERS

TIME	DRY	WET	DIRTY
	○	○	○
	○	○	○
	○	○	○
	○	○	○
	○	○	○
	○	○	○
	○	○	○
	○	○	○
	○	○	○
	○	○	○

FEEDING

TIME	OUNCES

SLEEP

START TIME	END TIME

PLAY

○ reading & language

○ music/singing

○ art/crafts/motor skills

○ playtime with toys

○ outdoor time

○ other: _____

SUPPLIES NEEDED

MEDICATIONS

TIME	TYPE & AMOUNT

NOTES TO PARENT

MOOD

○ happy   ○ fussy

○ sleepy   ○ sick

○ quiet   ○ grumpy

○ other _____

_____

DATE: _____ ○ Mon ○ Tue ○ Wed ○ Thur ○ Fri ○ Sat ○ Sun

NOTES TO NANNY _____

_____

| Wake Time | am | Last Fed At: | am |
| | pm | | pm |

DIAPERS

TIME	DRY	WET	DIRTY
	○	○	○
	○	○	○
	○	○	○
	○	○	○
	○	○	○
	○	○	○
	○	○	○
	○	○	○
	○	○	○
	○	○	○

FEEDING

TIME	OUNCES

SLEEP

START TIME	END TIME

PLAY

○ reading & language

○ music/singing

○ art/crafts/motor skills

○ playtime with toys

○ outdoor time

○ other: _____

SUPPLIES NEEDED

MEDICATIONS

TIME	TYPE & AMOUNT

NOTES TO PARENT

MOOD

○ happy ○ fussy

○ sleepy ○ sick

○ quiet ○ grumpy

○ other _____

_____

104

DATE: _____   ○ Mon ○ Tue ○ Wed ○ Thur ○ Fri ○ Sat ○ Sun

NOTES TO NANNY _____

Wake Time	am	Last Fed At:	am
	pm		pm

DIAPERS

TIME	DRY	WET	DIRTY
	○	○	○
	○	○	○
	○	○	○
	○	○	○
	○	○	○
	○	○	○
	○	○	○
	○	○	○
	○	○	○
	○	○	○

FEEDING

TIME	OUNCES

SLEEP

START TIME	END TIME

PLAY

○ reading & language

○ music/singing

○ art/crafts/motor skills

○ playtime with toys

○ outdoor time

○ other: _____

SUPPLIES NEEDED

MEDICATIONS

TIME	TYPE & AMOUNT

NOTES TO PARENT

MOOD

○ happy   ○ fussy

○ sleepy   ○ sick

○ quiet   ○ grumpy

○ other _____

DATE: _____ ○ Mon ○ Tue ○ Wed ○ Thur ○ Fri ○ Sat ○ Sun

NOTES TO NANNY _____

Wake Time	am	Last Fed At:	am
	pm		pm

DIAPERS

TIME	DRY	WET	DIRTY
	○	○	○
	○	○	○
	○	○	○
	○	○	○
	○	○	○
	○	○	○
	○	○	○
	○	○	○
	○	○	○
	○	○	○

FEEDING

TIME	OUNCES

SLEEP

START TIME	END TIME

PLAY

○ reading & language

○ music/singing

○ art/crafts/motor skills

○ playtime with toys

○ outdoor time

○ other: _____

SUPPLIES NEEDED

MEDICATIONS

TIME	TYPE & AMOUNT

NOTES TO PARENT

MOOD

○ happy   ○ fussy

○ sleepy   ○ sick

○ quiet   ○ grumpy

○ other: _____

DATE: _____   ○ Mon ○ Tue ○ Wed ○ Thur ○ Fri ○ Sat ○ Sun

NOTES TO NANNY _____

Wake Time	am	Last Fed At:	am
	pm		pm

DIAPERS

TIME	DRY	WET	DIRTY
	○	○	○
	○	○	○
	○	○	○
	○	○	○
	○	○	○
	○	○	○
	○	○	○
	○	○	○
	○	○	○
	○	○	○

FEEDING

TIME	OUNCES

SLEEP

START TIME	END TIME

PLAY

○ reading & language

○ music/singing

○ art/crafts/motor skills

○ playtime with toys

○ outdoor time

○ other: _____

SUPPLIES NEEDED

MEDICATIONS

TIME	TYPE & AMOUNT

NOTES TO PARENT

MOOD

○ happy   ○ fussy

○ sleepy   ○ sick

○ quiet   ○ grumpy

○ other _____

DATE: _____   ○ Mon ○ Tue ○ Wed ○ Thur ○ Fri ○ Sat ○ Sun

NOTES TO NANNY _____

Wake Time	am	Last Fed At:	am
	pm		pm

DIAPERS

TIME	DRY	WET	DIRTY
	○	○	○
	○	○	○
	○	○	○
	○	○	○
	○	○	○
	○	○	○
	○	○	○
	○	○	○
	○	○	○
	○	○	○

FEEDING

TIME	OUNCES

SLEEP

START TIME	END TIME

PLAY

○ reading & language

○ music/singing

○ art/crafts/motor skills

○ playtime with toys

○ outdoor time

○ other: _____

SUPPLIES NEEDED

MEDICATIONS

TIME	TYPE & AMOUNT

NOTES TO PARENT

MOOD

○ happy   ○ fussy

○ sleepy   ○ sick

○ quiet   ○ grumpy

○ other _____

DATE: _____   ○ Mon ○ Tue ○ Wed ○ Thur ○ Fri ○ Sat ○ Sun

NOTES TO NANNY _____

Wake Time	am	Last Fed At:	am
	pm		pm

DIAPERS			
TIME	DRY	WET	DIRTY
	○	○	○
	○	○	○
	○	○	○
	○	○	○
	○	○	○
	○	○	○
	○	○	○
	○	○	○
	○	○	○
	○	○	○

FEEDING	
TIME	OUNCES

SLEEP	
START TIME	END TIME

PLAY
○ reading & language
○ music/singing
○ art/crafts/motor skills
○ playtime with toys
○ outdoor time
○ other: _____

SUPPLIES NEEDED

MEDICATIONS	
TIME	TYPE & AMOUNT

NOTES TO PARENT

MOOD	
○ happy	○ fussy
○ sleepy	○ sick
○ quiet	○ grumpy
○ other	_____

DATE: _____   ○ Mon ○ Tue ○ Wed ○ Thur ○ Fri ○ Sat ○ Sun

NOTES TO NANNY _____

Wake Time	am	Last Fed At:	am
	pm		pm

DIAPERS

TIME	DRY	WET	DIRTY
	○	○	○
	○	○	○
	○	○	○
	○	○	○
	○	○	○
	○	○	○
	○	○	○
	○	○	○
	○	○	○
	○	○	○

FEEDING

TIME	OUNCES

SLEEP

START TIME	END TIME

PLAY

○ reading & language

○ music/singing

○ art/crafts/motor skills

○ playtime with toys

○ outdoor time

○ other:

SUPPLIES NEEDED

MEDICATIONS

TIME	TYPE & AMOUNT

NOTES TO PARENT

MOOD

○ happy   ○ fussy

○ sleepy   ○ sick

○ quiet   ○ grumpy

○ other _____

DATE: _____ ○ Mon ○ Tue ○ Wed ○ Thur ○ Fri ○ Sat ○ Sun

NOTES TO NANNY _____

Wake Time	am	Last Fed At:	am
	pm		pm

DIAPERS

TIME	DRY	WET	DIRTY
	○	○	○
	○	○	○
	○	○	○
	○	○	○
	○	○	○
	○	○	○
	○	○	○
	○	○	○
	○	○	○
	○	○	○

FEEDING

TIME	OUNCES

SLEEP

START TIME	END TIME

PLAY

○ reading & language
○ music/singing
○ art/crafts/motor skills
○ playtime with toys
○ outdoor time
○ other: _____

SUPPLIES NEEDED

MEDICATIONS

TIME	TYPE & AMOUNT

NOTES TO PARENT

MOOD

○ happy   ○ fussy
○ sleepy   ○ sick
○ quiet   ○ grumpy
○ other _____

DATE: _____   ○ Mon ○ Tue ○ Wed ○ Thur ○ Fri ○ Sat ○ Sun

NOTES TO NANNY _____

Wake Time	am	Last Fed At:	am
	pm		pm

DIAPERS			
TIME	DRY	WET	DIRTY
	○	○	○
	○	○	○
	○	○	○
	○	○	○
	○	○	○
	○	○	○
	○	○	○
	○	○	○
	○	○	○
	○	○	○

FEEDING	
TIME	OUNCES

SLEEP	
START TIME	END TIME

PLAY
○ reading & language
○ music/singing
○ art/crafts/motor skills
○ playtime with toys
○ outdoor time
○ other: _____

SUPPLIES NEEDED

MEDICATIONS	
TIME	TYPE & AMOUNT

NOTES TO PARENT

MOOD
○ happy ○ fussy
○ sleepy ○ sick
○ quiet ○ grumpy
○ other _____

DATE: _____ ○ Mon ○ Tue ○ Wed ○ Thur ○ Fri ○ Sat ○ Sun

NOTES TO NANNY _____

Wake Time	am	Last Fed At:	am
	pm		pm

DIAPERS

TIME	DRY	WET	DIRTY
	○	○	○
	○	○	○
	○	○	○
	○	○	○
	○	○	○
	○	○	○
	○	○	○
	○	○	○
	○	○	○
	○	○	○

FEEDING

TIME	OUNCES

SLEEP

START TIME	END TIME

PLAY

○ reading & language

○ music/singing

○ art/crafts/motor skills

○ playtime with toys

○ outdoor time

○ other: _____

SUPPLIES NEEDED

MEDICATIONS

TIME	TYPE & AMOUNT

NOTES TO PARENT

MOOD

○ happy   ○ fussy

○ sleepy   ○ sick

○ quiet   ○ grumpy

○ other _____

DATE: _____   ○ Mon ○ Tue ○ Wed ○ Thur ○ Fri ○ Sat ○ Sun

NOTES TO NANNY _____

_____

| Wake Time | am | Last Fed At: | am |
| | pm | | pm |

DIAPERS			
TIME	DRY	WET	DIRTY
	○	○	○
	○	○	○
	○	○	○
	○	○	○
	○	○	○
	○	○	○
	○	○	○
	○	○	○
	○	○	○
	○	○	○

FEEDING	
TIME	OUNCES

SLEEP	
START TIME	END TIME

PLAY
○ reading & language
○ music/singing
○ art/crafts/motor skills
○ playtime with toys
○ outdoor time
○ other: _____

SUPPLIES NEEDED

MEDICATIONS	
TIME	TYPE & AMOUNT

NOTES TO PARENT

MOOD	
○ happy	○ fussy
○ sleepy	○ sick
○ quiet	○ grumpy
○ other	_____

114

DATE: _____   ○ Mon ○ Tue ○ Wed ○ Thur ○ Fri ○ Sat ○ Sun

NOTES TO NANNY _____

| | Wake Time | am | Last Fed At: | am |
| | | pm | | pm |

DIAPERS

TIME	DRY	WET	DIRTY
	○	○	○
	○	○	○
	○	○	○
	○	○	○
	○	○	○
	○	○	○
	○	○	○
	○	○	○
	○	○	○
	○	○	○

FEEDING

TIME	OUNCES

SLEEP

START TIME	END TIME

PLAY

○ reading & language

○ music/singing

○ art/crafts/motor skills

○ playtime with toys

○ outdoor time

○ other: _____

SUPPLIES NEEDED

MEDICATIONS

TIME	TYPE & AMOUNT

NOTES TO PARENT

MOOD

○ happy   ○ fussy

○ sleepy   ○ sick

○ quiet   ○ grumpy

○ other   _____

_____

DATE: _____ ○ Mon ○ Tue ○ Wed ○ Thur ○ Fri ○ Sat ○ Sun

NOTES TO NANNY _____

Wake Time	am	Last Fed At:	am
	pm		pm

DIAPERS

TIME	DRY	WET	DIRTY
	○	○	○
	○	○	○
	○	○	○
	○	○	○
	○	○	○
	○	○	○
	○	○	○
	○	○	○
	○	○	○
	○	○	○

FEEDING

TIME	OUNCES

SLEEP

START TIME	END TIME

PLAY

○ reading & language

○ music/singing

○ art/crafts/motor skills

○ playtime with toys

○ outdoor time

○ other: _____

SUPPLIES NEEDED

MEDICATIONS

TIME	TYPE & AMOUNT

NOTES TO PARENT

MOOD

○ happy   ○ fussy

○ sleepy   ○ sick

○ quiet   ○ grumpy

○ other _____

DATE: _____   ○ Mon ○ Tue ○ Wed ○ Thur ○ Fri ○ Sat ○ Sun

NOTES TO NANNY _____

Wake Time	am	Last Fed At:	am
	pm		pm

DIAPERS

TIME	DRY	WET	DIRTY
	○	○	○
	○	○	○
	○	○	○
	○	○	○
	○	○	○
	○	○	○
	○	○	○
	○	○	○
	○	○	○
	○	○	○

FEEDING

TIME	OUNCES

SLEEP

START TIME	END TIME

PLAY

○ reading & language

○ music/singing

○ art/crafts/motor skills

○ playtime with toys

○ outdoor time

○ other: _____

SUPPLIES NEEDED

MEDICATIONS

TIME	TYPE & AMOUNT

NOTES TO PARENT

MOOD

○ happy   ○ fussy

○ sleepy   ○ sick

○ quiet   ○ grumpy

○ other _____

_____

DATE: _____   ○ Mon ○ Tue ○ Wed ○ Thur ○ Fri ○ Sat ○ Sun

NOTES TO NANNY _____

Wake Time	am	Last Fed At:	am
	pm		pm

DIAPERS

TIME	DRY	WET	DIRTY
	○	○	○
	○	○	○
	○	○	○
	○	○	○
	○	○	○
	○	○	○
	○	○	○
	○	○	○
	○	○	○
	○	○	○

FEEDING

TIME	OUNCES

SLEEP

START TIME	END TIME

PLAY

○ reading & language

○ music/singing

○ art/crafts/motor skills

○ playtime with toys

○ outdoor time

○ other: _____

SUPPLIES NEEDED

MEDICATIONS

TIME	TYPE & AMOUNT

NOTES TO PARENT

MOOD

○ happy   ○ fussy

○ sleepy   ○ sick

○ quiet   ○ grumpy

○ other   _____

DATE: _____   ◯ Mon ◯ Tue ◯ Wed ◯ Thur ◯ Fri ◯ Sat ◯ Sun

NOTES TO NANNY _____

	Wake Time	am	Last Fed At:	am
		pm		pm

DIAPERS			
TIME	DRY	WET	DIRTY
	◯	◯	◯
	◯	◯	◯
	◯	◯	◯
	◯	◯	◯
	◯	◯	◯
	◯	◯	◯
	◯	◯	◯
	◯	◯	◯
	◯	◯	◯
	◯	◯	◯

FEEDING	
TIME	OUNCES

SLEEP	
START TIME	END TIME

PLAY
◯ reading & language
◯ music/singing
◯ art/crafts/motor skills
◯ playtime with toys
◯ outdoor time
◯ other:

SUPPLIES NEEDED

MEDICATIONS	
TIME	TYPE & AMOUNT

NOTES TO PARENT

MOOD
◯ happy   ◯ fussy
◯ sleepy   ◯ sick
◯ quiet   ◯ grumpy
◯ other _____

DATE: _____   ○ Mon ○ Tue ○ Wed ○ Thur ○ Fri ○ Sat ○ Sun

NOTES TO NANNY _____

Wake Time	am	Last Fed At:	am
	pm		pm

DIAPERS			
TIME	DRY	WET	DIRTY
	○	○	○
	○	○	○
	○	○	○
	○	○	○
	○	○	○
	○	○	○
	○	○	○
	○	○	○
	○	○	○
	○	○	○

FEEDING	
TIME	OUNCES

SLEEP	
START TIME	END TIME

PLAY
○ reading & language
○ music/singing
○ art/crafts/motor skills
○ playtime with toys
○ outdoor time
○ other: _____

SUPPLIES NEEDED

MEDICATIONS	
TIME	TYPE & AMOUNT

NOTES TO PARENT

MOOD	
○ happy	○ fussy
○ sleepy	○ sick
○ quiet	○ grumpy
○ other	_____

DATE: _____ ○ Mon ○ Tue ○ Wed ○ Thur ○ Fri ○ Sat ○ Sun

NOTES TO NANNY _____

Wake Time	am	Last Fed At:	am
	pm		pm

DIAPERS			
TIME	DRY	WET	DIRTY
	○	○	○
	○	○	○
	○	○	○
	○	○	○
	○	○	○
	○	○	○
	○	○	○
	○	○	○
	○	○	○
	○	○	○

FEEDING	
TIME	OUNCES

SLEEP	
START TIME	END TIME

PLAY
○ reading & language
○ music/singing
○ art/crafts/motor skills
○ playtime with toys
○ outdoor time
○ other: _____

SUPPLIES NEEDED

MEDICATIONS	
TIME	TYPE & AMOUNT

NOTES TO PARENT

MOOD
○ happy   ○ fussy
○ sleepy ○ sick
○ quiet   ○ grumpy
○ other _____

DATE: _____   ○ Mon ○ Tue ○ Wed ○ Thur ○ Fri ○ Sat ○ Sun

NOTES TO NANNY _____

Wake Time	am	Last Fed At:	am
	pm		pm

DIAPERS

TIME	DRY	WET	DIRTY
	○	○	○
	○	○	○
	○	○	○
	○	○	○
	○	○	○
	○	○	○
	○	○	○
	○	○	○
	○	○	○
	○	○	○

FEEDING

TIME	OUNCES

SLEEP

START TIME	END TIME

PLAY

○ reading & language

○ music/singing

○ art/crafts/motor skills

○ playtime with toys

○ outdoor time

○ other: _____

SUPPLIES NEEDED

MEDICATIONS

TIME	TYPE & AMOUNT

NOTES TO PARENT

MOOD

○ happy   ○ fussy

○ sleepy   ○ sick

○ quiet   ○ grumpy

○ other   _____

DATE: _____   ○ Mon ○ Tue ○ Wed ○ Thur ○ Fri ○ Sat ○ Sun

NOTES TO NANNY _____

Wake Time	am	Last Fed At:	am
	pm		pm

DIAPERS

TIME	DRY	WET	DIRTY
	○	○	○
	○	○	○
	○	○	○
	○	○	○
	○	○	○
	○	○	○
	○	○	○
	○	○	○
	○	○	○
	○	○	○

FEEDING

TIME	OUNCES

SLEEP

START TIME	END TIME

PLAY

○ reading & language

○ music/singing

○ art/crafts/motor skills

○ playtime with toys

○ outdoor time

○ other: _____

SUPPLIES NEEDED

MEDICATIONS

TIME	TYPE & AMOUNT

NOTES TO PARENT

MOOD

○ happy   ○ fussy

○ sleepy   ○ sick

○ quiet   ○ grumpy

○ other _____

DATE: _____ ○ Mon ○ Tue ○ Wed ○ Thur ○ Fri ○ Sat ○ Sun

NOTES TO NANNY _____

Wake Time	am	Last Fed At:	am
	pm		pm

DIAPERS

TIME	DRY	WET	DIRTY
	○	○	○
	○	○	○
	○	○	○
	○	○	○
	○	○	○
	○	○	○
	○	○	○
	○	○	○
	○	○	○
	○	○	○

FEEDING

TIME	OUNCES

SLEEP

START TIME	END TIME

PLAY

○ reading & language

○ music/singing

○ art/crafts/motor skills

○ playtime with toys

○ outdoor time

○ other: _____

SUPPLIES NEEDED

MEDICATIONS

TIME	TYPE & AMOUNT

NOTES TO PARENT

MOOD

○ happy   ○ fussy

○ sleepy   ○ sick

○ quiet   ○ grumpy

○ other _____

_____

DATE: _____ ○ Mon ○ Tue ○ Wed ○ Thur ○ Fri ○ Sat ○ Sun

NOTES TO NANNY _____

| | Wake Time | am | Last Fed At: | am |
| | | pm | | pm |

DIAPERS

TIME	DRY	WET	DIRTY
	○	○	○
	○	○	○
	○	○	○
	○	○	○
	○	○	○
	○	○	○
	○	○	○
	○	○	○
	○	○	○
	○	○	○

FEEDING

TIME	OUNCES

SLEEP

START TIME	END TIME

PLAY

○ reading & language

○ music/singing

○ art/crafts/motor skills

○ playtime with toys

○ outdoor time

○ other: _____

SUPPLIES NEEDED

MEDICATIONS

TIME	TYPE & AMOUNT

NOTES TO PARENT

MOOD

○ happy   ○ fussy

○ sleepy   ○ sick

○ quiet   ○ grumpy

○ other _____

125

DATE: _____   ◯ Mon ◯ Tue ◯ Wed ◯ Thur ◯ Fri ◯ Sat ◯ Sun

NOTES TO NANNY _____

Wake Time	am	Last Fed At:	am
	pm		pm

DIAPERS

TIME	DRY	WET	DIRTY
	◯	◯	◯
	◯	◯	◯
	◯	◯	◯
	◯	◯	◯
	◯	◯	◯
	◯	◯	◯
	◯	◯	◯
	◯	◯	◯
	◯	◯	◯
	◯	◯	◯

FEEDING

TIME	OUNCES

SLEEP

START TIME	END TIME

PLAY

◯ reading & language

◯ music/singing

◯ art/crafts/motor skills

◯ playtime with toys

◯ outdoor time

◯ other: _____

SUPPLIES NEEDED

MEDICATIONS

TIME	TYPE & AMOUNT

NOTES TO PARENT

MOOD

◯ happy   ◯ fussy

◯ sleepy   ◯ sick

◯ quiet   ◯ grumpy

◯ other   _____

DATE: _____ ○ Mon ○ Tue ○ Wed ○ Thur ○ Fri ○ Sat ○ Sun

NOTES TO NANNY _____

_____

Wake Time	am	Last Fed At:	am
	pm		pm

DIAPERS

TIME	DRY	WET	DIRTY
	○	○	○
	○	○	○
	○	○	○
	○	○	○
	○	○	○
	○	○	○
	○	○	○
	○	○	○
	○	○	○
	○	○	○

FEEDING

TIME	OUNCES

SLEEP

START TIME	END TIME

PLAY

○ reading & language

○ music/singing

○ art/crafts/motor skills

○ playtime with toys

○ outdoor time

○ other: _____

SUPPLIES NEEDED

MEDICATIONS

TIME	TYPE & AMOUNT

NOTES TO PARENT

MOOD

○ happy   ○ fussy

○ sleepy   ○ sick

○ quiet   ○ grumpy

○ other _____

_____

DATE: _____   ○ Mon ○ Tue ○ Wed ○ Thur ○ Fri ○ Sat ○ Sun

NOTES TO NANNY _____

_____

Wake Time	am	Last Fed At:	am
	pm		pm

DIAPERS			
TIME	DRY	WET	DIRTY
	○	○	○
	○	○	○
	○	○	○
	○	○	○
	○	○	○
	○	○	○
	○	○	○
	○	○	○
	○	○	○
	○	○	○

FEEDING	
TIME	OUNCES

SLEEP	
START TIME	END TIME

PLAY
○ reading & language
○ music/singing
○ art/crafts/motor skills
○ playtime with toys
○ outdoor time
○ other: _____

SUPPLIES NEEDED

MEDICATIONS	
TIME	TYPE & AMOUNT

NOTES TO PARENT

MOOD	
○ happy	○ fussy
○ sleepy	○ sick
○ quiet	○ grumpy
○ other	_____

DATE: _____ ○ Mon ○ Tue ○ Wed ○ Thur ○ Fri ○ Sat ○ Sun

NOTES TO NANNY _____

	Wake Time	am	Last Fed At:	am
		pm		pm

DIAPERS			
TIME	DRY	WET	DIRTY
	○	○	○
	○	○	○
	○	○	○
	○	○	○
	○	○	○
	○	○	○
	○	○	○
	○	○	○
	○	○	○
	○	○	○

FEEDING	
TIME	OUNCES

SLEEP	
START TIME	END TIME

PLAY
○ reading & language
○ music/singing
○ art/crafts/motor skills
○ playtime with toys
○ outdoor time
○ other: _____

SUPPLIES NEEDED

MEDICATIONS	
TIME	TYPE & AMOUNT

NOTES TO PARENT

MOOD
○ happy   ○ fussy
○ sleepy   ○ sick
○ quiet   ○ grumpy
○ other _____

DATE: _____ ○ Mon ○ Tue ○ Wed ○ Thur ○ Fri ○ Sat ○ Sun

NOTES TO NANNY _____

Wake Time	am	Last Fed At:	am
	pm		pm

DIAPERS

TIME	DRY	WET	DIRTY
	○	○	○
	○	○	○
	○	○	○
	○	○	○
	○	○	○
	○	○	○
	○	○	○
	○	○	○
	○	○	○
	○	○	○

FEEDING

TIME	OUNCES

SLEEP

START TIME	END TIME

PLAY

○ reading & language

○ music/singing

○ art/crafts/motor skills

○ playtime with toys

○ outdoor time

○ other: _____

SUPPLIES NEEDED

MEDICATIONS

TIME	TYPE & AMOUNT

NOTES TO PARENT

MOOD

○ happy   ○ fussy

○ sleepy   ○ sick

○ quiet   ○ grumpy

○ other _____

DATE: _____ ○ Mon ○ Tue ○ Wed ○ Thur ○ Fri ○ Sat ○ Sun

NOTES TO NANNY _____

Wake Time	am	Last Fed At:	am
	pm		pm

DIAPERS			
TIME	DRY	WET	DIRTY
	○	○	○
	○	○	○
	○	○	○
	○	○	○
	○	○	○
	○	○	○
	○	○	○
	○	○	○
	○	○	○
	○	○	○

FEEDING	
TIME	OUNCES

SLEEP	
START TIME	END TIME

PLAY

○ reading & language

○ music/singing

○ art/crafts/motor skills

○ playtime with toys

○ outdoor time

○ other: _____

SUPPLIES NEEDED

MEDICATIONS	
TIME	TYPE & AMOUNT

NOTES TO PARENT

MOOD

○ happy ○ fussy

○ sleepy ○ sick

○ quiet ○ grumpy

○ other _____

_____

DATE: _____   ○ Mon ○ Tue ○ Wed ○ Thur ○ Fri ○ Sat ○ Sun

NOTES TO NANNY _____

Wake Time	am	Last Fed At:	am
	pm		pm

DIAPERS			
TIME	DRY	WET	DIRTY
	○	○	○
	○	○	○
	○	○	○
	○	○	○
	○	○	○
	○	○	○
	○	○	○
	○	○	○
	○	○	○
	○	○	○

FEEDING	
TIME	OUNCES

SLEEP	
START TIME	END TIME

PLAY

○ reading & language

○ music/singing

○ art/crafts/motor skills

○ playtime with toys

○ outdoor time

○ other: _____

SUPPLIES NEEDED

MEDICATIONS

TIME	TYPE & AMOUNT

NOTES TO PARENT

MOOD

○ happy   ○ fussy

○ sleepy   ○ sick

○ quiet   ○ grumpy

○ other   _____

_____

132

DATE: _____   ○ Mon ○ Tue ○ Wed ○ Thur ○ Fri ○ Sat ○ Sun

NOTES TO NANNY _____

Wake Time	am	Last Fed At:	am
	pm		pm

DIAPERS

TIME	DRY	WET	DIRTY
	○	○	○
	○	○	○
	○	○	○
	○	○	○
	○	○	○
	○	○	○
	○	○	○
	○	○	○
	○	○	○
	○	○	○

FEEDING

TIME	OUNCES

SLEEP

START TIME	END TIME

PLAY

○ reading & language

○ music/singing

○ art/crafts/motor skills

○ playtime with toys

○ outdoor time

○ other: _____

SUPPLIES NEEDED

MEDICATIONS

TIME	TYPE & AMOUNT

NOTES TO PARENT

MOOD

○ happy   ○ fussy

○ sleepy   ○ sick

○ quiet   ○ grumpy

○ other _____

DATE: _____   ○ Mon ○ Tue ○ Wed ○ Thur ○ Fri ○ Sat ○ Sun

NOTES TO NANNY _____

Wake Time	am	Last Fed At:	am
	pm		pm

DIAPERS			
TIME	DRY	WET	DIRTY
	○	○	○
	○	○	○
	○	○	○
	○	○	○
	○	○	○
	○	○	○
	○	○	○
	○	○	○
	○	○	○
	○	○	○

FEEDING	
TIME	OUNCES

SLEEP	
START TIME	END TIME

PLAY
○ reading & language
○ music/singing
○ art/crafts/motor skills
○ playtime with toys
○ outdoor time
○ other: _____

SUPPLIES NEEDED

MEDICATIONS	
TIME	TYPE & AMOUNT

NOTES TO PARENT

MOOD	
○ happy	○ fussy
○ sleepy	○ sick
○ quiet	○ grumpy
○ other	_____

DATE: _____ ○ Mon ○ Tue ○ Wed ○ Thur ○ Fri ○ Sat ○ Sun

NOTES TO NANNY _____

_____

_____

| Wake Time | am | Last Fed At: | am |
| | pm | | pm |

DIAPERS			
TIME	DRY	WET	DIRTY
	○	○	○
	○	○	○
	○	○	○
	○	○	○
	○	○	○
	○	○	○
	○	○	○
	○	○	○
	○	○	○
	○	○	○

FEEDING	
TIME	OUNCES

SLEEP	
START TIME	END TIME

PLAY

○ reading & language

○ music/singing

○ art/crafts/motor skills

○ playtime with toys

○ outdoor time

○ other: _____

SUPPLIES NEEDED

MEDICATIONS	
TIME	TYPE & AMOUNT

NOTES TO PARENT

MOOD

○ happy   ○ fussy

○ sleepy   ○ sick

○ quiet   ○ grumpy

○ other _____

_____

DATE: _____ ○ Mon ○ Tue ○ Wed ○ Thur ○ Fri ○ Sat ○ Sun

NOTES TO NANNY _____

_____

Wake Time	am	Last Fed At:	am
	pm		pm

DIAPERS

TIME	DRY	WET	DIRTY
	○	○	○
	○	○	○
	○	○	○
	○	○	○
	○	○	○
	○	○	○
	○	○	○
	○	○	○
	○	○	○
	○	○	○

FEEDING

TIME	OUNCES

SLEEP

START TIME	END TIME

PLAY

○ reading & language

○ music/singing

○ art/crafts/motor skills

○ playtime with toys

○ outdoor time

○ other: _____

SUPPLIES NEEDED

MEDICATIONS

TIME	TYPE & AMOUNT

NOTES TO PARENT

MOOD

○ happy ○ fussy

○ sleepy ○ sick

○ quiet ○ grumpy

○ other _____

_____

DATE: _____   ○ Mon ○ Tue ○ Wed ○ Thur ○ Fri ○ Sat ○ Sun

NOTES TO NANNY _____

Wake Time	am	Last Fed At:	am
	pm		pm

DIAPERS			
TIME	DRY	WET	DIRTY
	○	○	○
	○	○	○
	○	○	○
	○	○	○
	○	○	○
	○	○	○
	○	○	○
	○	○	○
	○	○	○
	○	○	○

FEEDING	
TIME	OUNCES

SLEEP	
START TIME	END TIME

PLAY

○ reading & language

○ music/singing

○ art/crafts/motor skills

○ playtime with toys

○ outdoor time

○ other: _____

SUPPLIES NEEDED

MEDICATIONS	
TIME	TYPE & AMOUNT

NOTES TO PARENT

MOOD

○ happy   ○ fussy

○ sleepy   ○ sick

○ quiet   ○ grumpy

○ other _____

DATE: _____   ○ Mon ○ Tue ○ Wed ○ Thur ○ Fri ○ Sat ○ Sun

NOTES TO NANNY _____

Wake Time	am	Last Fed At:	am
	pm		pm

DIAPERS			
TIME	DRY	WET	DIRTY
	○	○	○
	○	○	○
	○	○	○
	○	○	○
	○	○	○
	○	○	○
	○	○	○
	○	○	○
	○	○	○
	○	○	○

FEEDING	
TIME	OUNCES

SLEEP	
START TIME	END TIME

PLAY
○ reading & language
○ music/singing
○ art/crafts/motor skills
○ playtime with toys
○ outdoor time
○ other: _____

SUPPLIES NEEDED

MEDICATIONS	
TIME	TYPE & AMOUNT

NOTES TO PARENT

MOOD
○ happy ○ fussy
○ sleepy ○ sick
○ quiet ○ grumpy
○ other _____

DATE: _____ ○ Mon ○ Tue ○ Wed ○ Thur ○ Fri ○ Sat ○ Sun

NOTES TO NANNY _____

_____

Wake Time	am	Last Fed At:	am
	pm		pm

DIAPERS

TIME	DRY	WET	DIRTY
	○	○	○
	○	○	○
	○	○	○
	○	○	○
	○	○	○
	○	○	○
	○	○	○
	○	○	○
	○	○	○
	○	○	○

FEEDING

TIME	OUNCES

SLEEP

START TIME	END TIME

PLAY

○ reading & language

○ music/singing

○ art/crafts/motor skills

○ playtime with toys

○ outdoor time

○ other: _____

SUPPLIES NEEDED

MEDICATIONS

TIME	TYPE & AMOUNT

NOTES TO PARENT

MOOD

○ happy   ○ fussy

○ sleepy   ○ sick

○ quiet   ○ grumpy

○ other _____

_____

DATE: _____   ○ Mon ○ Tue ○ Wed ○ Thur ○ Fri ○ Sat ○ Sun

NOTES TO NANNY _____

| Wake Time | am | Last Fed At: | am |
| | pm | | pm |

DIAPERS

TIME	DRY	WET	DIRTY
	○	○	○
	○	○	○
	○	○	○
	○	○	○
	○	○	○
	○	○	○
	○	○	○
	○	○	○
	○	○	○
	○	○	○

FEEDING

TIME	OUNCES

SLEEP

START TIME	END TIME

PLAY

○ reading & language

○ music/singing

○ art/crafts/motor skills

○ playtime with toys

○ outdoor time

○ other: _____

SUPPLIES NEEDED

MEDICATIONS

TIME	TYPE & AMOUNT

NOTES TO PARENT

MOOD

○ happy   ○ fussy

○ sleepy   ○ sick

○ quiet   ○ grumpy

○ other _____

DATE: _____ ○ Mon ○ Tue ○ Wed ○ Thur ○ Fri ○ Sat ○ Sun

NOTES TO NANNY _____

Wake Time	am	Last Fed At:	am
	pm		pm

DIAPERS

TIME	DRY	WET	DIRTY
	○	○	○
	○	○	○
	○	○	○
	○	○	○
	○	○	○
	○	○	○
	○	○	○
	○	○	○
	○	○	○
	○	○	○

FEEDING

TIME	OUNCES

SLEEP

START TIME	END TIME

PLAY

○ reading & language

○ music/singing

○ art/crafts/motor skills

○ playtime with toys

○ outdoor time

○ other: _____

SUPPLIES NEEDED

MEDICATIONS

TIME	TYPE & AMOUNT

NOTES TO PARENT

MOOD

○ happy   ○ fussy

○ sleepy   ○ sick

○ quiet   ○ grumpy

○ other _____

DATE: _____ ○ Mon ○ Tue ○ Wed ○ Thur ○ Fri ○ Sat ○ Sun

NOTES TO NANNY _____

Wake Time	am	Last Fed At:	am
	pm		pm

DIAPERS			
TIME	DRY	WET	DIRTY
	○	○	○
	○	○	○
	○	○	○
	○	○	○
	○	○	○
	○	○	○
	○	○	○
	○	○	○
	○	○	○
	○	○	○

FEEDING	
TIME	OUNCES

SLEEP	
START TIME	END TIME

PLAY

○ reading & language

○ music/singing

○ art/crafts/motor skills

○ playtime with toys

○ outdoor time

○ other: _____

SUPPLIES NEEDED

MEDICATIONS	
TIME	TYPE & AMOUNT

NOTES TO PARENT

MOOD

○ happy   ○ fussy

○ sleepy   ○ sick

○ quiet   ○ grumpy

○ other _____

DATE: _____ ○ Mon ○ Tue ○ Wed ○ Thur ○ Fri ○ Sat ○ Sun

NOTES TO NANNY _____

Wake Time	am	Last Fed At:	am
	pm		pm

DIAPERS			
TIME	DRY	WET	DIRTY
	○	○	○
	○	○	○
	○	○	○
	○	○	○
	○	○	○
	○	○	○
	○	○	○
	○	○	○
	○	○	○
	○	○	○

FEEDING	
TIME	OUNCES

SLEEP	
START TIME	END TIME

PLAY

○ reading & language

○ music/singing

○ art/crafts/motor skills

○ playtime with toys

○ outdoor time

○ other: _____

SUPPLIES NEEDED

MEDICATIONS	
TIME	TYPE & AMOUNT

NOTES TO PARENT

MOOD

○ happy   ○ fussy

○ sleepy   ○ sick

○ quiet   ○ grumpy

○ other _____

143

DATE: _____   ○ Mon ○ Tue ○ Wed ○ Thur ○ Fri ○ Sat ○ Sun

NOTES TO NANNY _____

_____

Wake Time	am	Last Fed At:	am
	pm		pm

DIAPERS

TIME	DRY	WET	DIRTY
	○	○	○
	○	○	○
	○	○	○
	○	○	○
	○	○	○
	○	○	○
	○	○	○
	○	○	○
	○	○	○
	○	○	○

FEEDING

TIME	OUNCES

SLEEP

START TIME	END TIME

PLAY

○ reading & language

○ music/singing

○ art/crafts/motor skills

○ playtime with toys

○ outdoor time

○ other: _____

SUPPLIES NEEDED

MEDICATIONS

TIME	TYPE & AMOUNT

NOTES TO PARENT

MOOD

○ happy ○ fussy

○ sleepy ○ sick

○ quiet ○ grumpy

○ other _____

DATE: _____ ○ Mon ○ Tue ○ Wed ○ Thur ○ Fri ○ Sat ○ Sun

NOTES TO NANNY _____

Wake Time	am	Last Fed At:	am
	pm		pm

DIAPERS			
TIME	DRY	WET	DIRTY
	○	○	○
	○	○	○
	○	○	○
	○	○	○
	○	○	○
	○	○	○
	○	○	○
	○	○	○
	○	○	○
	○	○	○

FEEDING	
TIME	OUNCES

SLEEP	
START TIME	END TIME

PLAY
○ reading & language
○ music/singing
○ art/crafts/motor skills
○ playtime with toys
○ outdoor time
○ other: _____

SUPPLIES NEEDED

MEDICATIONS	
TIME	TYPE & AMOUNT

NOTES TO PARENT

MOOD
○ happy   ○ fussy
○ sleepy   ○ sick
○ quiet   ○ grumpy
○ other _____

DATE: _____   ○ Mon ○ Tue ○ Wed ○ Thur ○ Fri ○ Sat ○ Sun

NOTES TO NANNY _____

Wake Time	am	Last Fed At:	am
	pm		pm

DIAPERS			
TIME	DRY	WET	DIRTY
	○	○	○
	○	○	○
	○	○	○
	○	○	○
	○	○	○
	○	○	○
	○	○	○
	○	○	○
	○	○	○
	○	○	○

FEEDING	
TIME	OUNCES

SLEEP	
START TIME	END TIME

PLAY
○ reading & language
○ music/singing
○ art/crafts/motor skills
○ playtime with toys
○ outdoor time
○ other: _____

SUPPLIES NEEDED

MEDICATIONS	
TIME	TYPE & AMOUNT

NOTES TO PARENT

MOOD	
○ happy	○ fussy
○ sleepy	○ sick
○ quiet	○ grumpy
○ other	_____

DATE: _____   ○ Mon ○ Tue ○ Wed ○ Thur ○ Fri ○ Sat ○ Sun

NOTES TO NANNY _____

Wake Time	am	Last Fed At:	am
	pm		pm

DIAPERS			
TIME	DRY	WET	DIRTY
	○	○	○
	○	○	○
	○	○	○
	○	○	○
	○	○	○
	○	○	○
	○	○	○
	○	○	○
	○	○	○
	○	○	○

FEEDING	
TIME	OUNCES

SLEEP	
START TIME	END TIME

PLAY
○ reading & language
○ music/singing
○ art/crafts/motor skills
○ playtime with toys
○ outdoor time
○ other: _____

SUPPLIES NEEDED

MEDICATIONS	
TIME	TYPE & AMOUNT

NOTES TO PARENT

MOOD
○ happy   ○ fussy
○ sleepy   ○ sick
○ quiet   ○ grumpy
○ other _____

DATE: _____   ○ Mon ○ Tue ○ Wed ○ Thur ○ Fri ○ Sat ○ Sun

NOTES TO NANNY _____

| Wake Time | am | Last Fed At: | am |
| | pm | | pm |

DIAPERS

TIME	DRY	WET	DIRTY
	○	○	○
	○	○	○
	○	○	○
	○	○	○
	○	○	○
	○	○	○
	○	○	○
	○	○	○
	○	○	○
	○	○	○

FEEDING

TIME	OUNCES

SLEEP

START TIME	END TIME

PLAY

○ reading & language

○ music/singing

○ art/crafts/motor skills

○ playtime with toys

○ outdoor time

○ other: _____

SUPPLIES NEEDED

MEDICATIONS

TIME	TYPE & AMOUNT

NOTES TO PARENT

MOOD

○ happy ○ fussy

○ sleepy ○ sick

○ quiet ○ grumpy

○ other _____

DATE: _____ ○ Mon ○ Tue ○ Wed ○ Thur ○ Fri ○ Sat ○ Sun

NOTES TO NANNY _____

_____

Wake Time	am	Last Fed At:	am
	pm		pm

DIAPERS			
TIME	DRY	WET	DIRTY
	○	○	○
	○	○	○
	○	○	○
	○	○	○
	○	○	○
	○	○	○
	○	○	○
	○	○	○
	○	○	○
	○	○	○

FEEDING	
TIME	OUNCES

SLEEP	
START TIME	END TIME

PLAY
○ reading & language
○ music/singing
○ art/crafts/motor skills
○ playtime with toys
○ outdoor time
○ other:

SUPPLIES NEEDED

MEDICATIONS	
TIME	TYPE & AMOUNT

NOTES TO PARENT

MOOD
○ happy   ○ fussy
○ sleepy   ○ sick
○ quiet   ○ grumpy
○ other _____

DATE: _____   ○ Mon ○ Tue ○ Wed ○ Thur ○ Fri ○ Sat ○ Sun

NOTES TO NANNY _____

Wake Time	am	Last Fed At:	am
	pm		pm

DIAPERS

TIME	DRY	WET	DIRTY
	○	○	○
	○	○	○
	○	○	○
	○	○	○
	○	○	○
	○	○	○
	○	○	○
	○	○	○
	○	○	○
	○	○	○

FEEDING

TIME	OUNCES

SLEEP

START TIME	END TIME

PLAY

○ reading & language

○ music/singing

○ art/crafts/motor skills

○ playtime with toys

○ outdoor time

○ other: _____

SUPPLIES NEEDED

MEDICATIONS

TIME	TYPE & AMOUNT

NOTES TO PARENT

MOOD

○ happy   ○ fussy

○ sleepy   ○ sick

○ quiet   ○ grumpy

○ other   _____

Made in the USA
Monee, IL
01 June 2023

35067030R00083